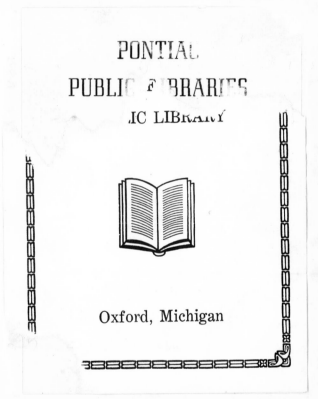

Y Is for Verses

❀ ODILLE OUSLEY ❀

GINN AND COMPANY

Acknowledgments

Grateful acknowledgment is made to the following authors, copyright owners, and publishers for permission to use the poems in this book:

Abelard-Schuman, Ltd. for "After the End," "Cowboy Hats," "Fall," and "Just a Mile Beyond," reprinted from *Runny Days, Sunny Days* by Aileen Fisher, copyright, 1958, by Abelard-Schuman, Ltd.; and for "A Spike of Green," by Barbara Baker, reprinted from *Poems and Pictures* by K. M. Lines and N. Montgomerie, copyright, 1959, by Abelard-Schuman, Ltd. By permission of Abelard-Schuman, Ltd. All rights reserved.

Abingdon Press for "Winds A'Blowing," from the book *Winds A'Blowing* by May Justus. Copyright © 1940, by May Justus, 1961, by Abingdon Press; for "The Three Horses," from *I Rode the Black Horse Far Away* by Ivy O. Eastwick. Copyright © 1960, by Abingdon Press; for "Sneakers," and "Mittens," from *Once Upon a Season* by Lilian Moore. Copyright © 1962, by Abingdon Press.

The American Baptist Publication Society for "Neighbors," by Rebecca K. Sprinkle, and "New Kittens," by Grace Noll Crowell from *Story World*, permission of the American Baptist Publication Society.

Appleton-Century-Crofts, Inc. for "The Elf and the Dormouse," from *Artful Antics* by Oliver Herford, copyright, 1901, by Appleton-Century-Crofts, Inc.; and for "Snowflakes," by Mary Mapes Dodge from *St. Nicholas Magazine*. Reprinted by permission of Appleton-Century-Crofts, Inc.

Dorothy W. Baruch for her poems "The Elevator," and "Automobile Mechanics," from *I Like Machinery*, published by Harper & Brothers, copyright, 1933.

Basil Blackwell & Mott, Ltd. for "Plans," from *The Merry-Go-Round* by Luisa Hewitt.

Rowena Bennett for "Vacation Time," and Naida Dickson for "The Jet" in *The Instructor* magazine, published by the F. A. Owen Publishing Company.

Board of Christian Education, Presbyterian Church in the United States and the authors for "Pablo Has a Donkey," by Nona Keen Duffy, and "The Shop Across the Street," by Mary A. Gilliam, in *The Story Hour*, published by Board of Christian Education, Presbyterian Church in the United States.

The Bodley Head, Ltd. for "I Meant to Do My Work Today," from *The Lonely Dancer* by Richard Le Gallienne, copyright, 1913, 1941, by Richard Le Gallienne. Reprinted by permission of The Bodley Head, Ltd.

Lourena Renton Brown for her poem "Candle Star," reprinted by permission from the November issue of *Good Housekeeping*. © 1959, by the Hearst Corporation.

Maud Burnham for her poem "The Barnyard," from *Rhymes for Little Hands*, published by Milton Bradley Co.

Child Life magazine, the authors, and copyright owners for the poems: "Three Little Turtles," by Vivian G. Gouled, and "Gardening," by Anne Zuker, copyright, 1950; "The Neck," by Ilo Orleans, copyright, 1951; "What, Oh What?" by Ilo Orleans, copyright, 1952; "Street Mending," by Dorothy Faubion, permission of Dr. L. Ray Faubion, "Rides," by Ilo Orleans, and "Cowboy Song," by Nona Keen Duffy, copyright, 1953; "I Held a Lamb," by Kim Worthington, copyright, 1954; "Names," by Naida Dickson, "High Top Boots," by Nona Keen Duffy, and "Open the Gift," by Regina Sauro, copyright, 1955; "Pussy Feet," by Ruth Chandler, "The Friendly Ocean," by Ernest Holbrook, "September Morning," by Katherine Edelman, "School," by Florence Logee, "Shhhh!," by Grace A. Stephens, and "Playtime," by Edna Gray B. MacDonald, copyright, 1956; "My Top," by Jeanne L. Kenyon, and "Little Goldfish," by Regina Sauro, copyright, 1958; "Kite Song," by Avan Collum, the lines from "The Artist," by Wallace M. Kelly, "Chicks," by Ilo Orleans, "My Rocket Ship," by Frances G. Risser, and "April Shower," by Emily H. Watson, copyright, 1959; "Fun from A to Z," by Frances Copley, copyright, 1961. All from *Child Life* magazine.

William Collins Sons & Company, Ltd. for "Keep a poem in your pocket" ("At Night"), and "What's the funniest thing you can think of?" ("The Funniest Thing"), from *Something Special* by Beatrice Schenk de Regniers.

Curtis Brown, Ltd. and the author for the alphabet rhymes "E," "Q," "U," and "X," from *All Around the Town* by Phyllis McGinley, copyright, 1948, by Phyllis McGinley, reprinted by permission of the author.

J. M. Dent & Sons, Ltd. for "The Camel," and "The Kitten," from *Verses From 1929 On* by Ogden Nash.

Dodd, Mead & Company for "I Meant to Do My Work Today," reprinted by permission of Dodd, Mead & Company from *The Lonely Dancer* by Richard Le Gallienne, copyright, 1913, 1941, by Richard Le Gallienne.

Doubleday & Company, Inc. for "A Birthday," "Circus Day," and "Halloween," from *A Little Book of Days* by Rachel Field. Copyright, 1927, by Doubleday & Company, Inc.; "The Animal Store," and "Vegetables," from *Taxis and Toadstools* by Rachel Field. Copyright, 1926, by Doubleday & Company, Inc.; "The Barge," "The New Neighbor," and "Shop Windows," from *Gay Go Up* by Rose Fyleman. Copyright, 1929, 1930, by Doubleday & Company, Inc.; "The Apple Tree," from *The Fairy Flute* by Rose Fyleman. Copyright, 1923, by Doubleday & Company, Inc.; "Uncle Frank," from *Goose Grass Rhymes* by Monica Shannon. Copyright, 1930, by Doubleday & Company, Inc.; "Letter to a Robin in March," from *Poems for Josephine* by Kathryn Worth. Copyright, 1943, by Kathryn Worth Curry. All reprinted by permission of Doubleday & Company, Inc.

Gerald Duckworth & Company, Ltd., London, for permission to reprint "Friday Street," from *Nursery Rhymes of London Town* by Eleanor Farjeon, and for "The Elephant," from *Cautionary Verses* by Hilaire Belloc.

Nona Keen Duffy, the author, for "Airplane" published in the *Grade Teacher* magazine, copyright, 1952.

E. P. Dutton & Company, Inc. for "Furry Bear," and "Wind on the Hill," from the longer poem "Wind on the Hill," from *Now We Are Six* by A. A. Milne. Copyright, 1927, by E. P. Dutton & Company, Inc. Renewal, 1955, by A. A. Milne; "Missing," and "At the Zoo," from *When We Were Very Young* by A. A. Milne. Copyright, 1924, by E. P. Dutton & Company, Inc. Renewal, 1952, by A. A. Milne; "The House of the Mouse," "It Is Raining," from the longer poem "It Is Raining," and "Work Horses," from *Another Here and Now Story Book* by Lucy Sprague Mitchell. Copyright, 1937, by E. P. Dutton & Company, Inc.; "If I Had Two Apples," from the longer poem "Wishing," from *Me* by Inez Hogan. Copyright, 1954, by Inez Hogan; "The New Umbrella," and "Tricycle," from *Stories to Begin On* by Rhoda W. Bacmeister. Copyright, 1940, by E. P. Dutton & Company, Inc.; all reprinted by permission of the publishers; "Cleverness," and "Our Tree," copyright, 1941, by Marchette Chute. From the book *Around and About* by Marchette Chute, published, 1957, by E. P. Dutton & Company, Inc., and reprinted with their permission; "Art," "Portrait," and "Playing Ball," copyright, 1946, by Marchette Chute. From the book *Around and About* by Marchette Chute. Published, 1957, by E. P. Dutton & Company, Inc., and reprinted with their permission. "Mail," and "Park Bench," copyright, 1946, by Marchette Chute. From her book *Rhymes About the City*. Reprinted by permission of the author. "Day Before Christmas," copyright, 1941, by Marchette Chute. From her book *Rhymes About the Country*. Reprinted by permission of the author.

Ivy O. Eastwick, the author, for "Seven Today," from *Birthday Candles Burning Bright*, compiled by Sara and John E. Brewton, copyright, 1960, published by The Macmillan Company; "Winter in the Wood," from *Year Around: Poems for Children* edited by Alice I. Hazeltine and Elva S. Smith, copyright, 1956, published by Abingdon Press; "A Country Child's Prayer," and "Nonsense Verses" ("Two Little Dragons"), in *Jack and Jill* magazine, reprinted by

iv

To the memory of my mother and my father
who shared their pleasure
in some of these same verses
with the little girl I used to be

Poems about . . .

A—Airplanes

Airplane

Zoom! Zoom!
   High over head
Hums a plane
   Of gleaming red.

Hums a glowing,
   Gleaming ship,
Making some
   Exciting trip!

Nona Keen Duffy

The Airplane

The airplane taxis down the field
And heads into the breeze,
It lifts its wheels above the ground,
It skims above the trees,
It rises high and higher
Away up toward the sun,
It's just a speck against the sky
      —And now it's gone!

Author Unknown

At the Airport

Higher
than
higher
than
higher
than heaven,

Up goes the gray of the DC–7,

Up go the wheels and the tail is gone
In a bright pink cloud of the flying dawn. . . .

Myra Cohn Livingston

Up in the Air

Zooming across the sky,
Like a great bird you fly,
   Airplane,
   Silvery white
   In the light.

Turning and twisting in the air,
When shall I ever be there,
   Airplane,
   Piloting you
   Far in the blue?

James S. Tippett

The Jet

Hear the jet,
The loud old jet!
Just how noisy can it get?
Screaming by,
Streaming high,
Loud and raucous, splits the sky!

See the jet,
The speedy jet!
In all the world, the fastest yet!
Here, then gone,
Streaking on—
Spans the world from dawn to dawn!

Naida Dickson

Air Station

My rocket ship will travel fast,
And it will travel far.
I'll cruise in it to planets
And to the farthest star.

Then, when I've traveled all about,
A station in the air
Will give my ship a checkup,
And I'll start home from there.

Emily M. Hilsabeck

Something to Think About

When airplanes get as thick as cars,
And people ride from earth to Mars,
Will traffic lights be made of stars?

Carolyn Forsyth

A—Apples

Apple Blossoms

The apple blossoms grow so high
  Upon the branches of our tree,
I can't reach up to smell them; so
  They send their perfume down to me.

Helen Wing

Green-Apple Morning

It's a green-apple morning,
Polished with sun,
And here in the orchard
Mist is spun.
The sun's red crayon
Paints the hill
While orchard trees stand
Picture-still.
I run to the edge of
This new day,
And the green-apple morning
Slips away.

Mary Graham Bond

Ripe Apples

The orchard's
Like a fairyland,
With apples ripe
On every hand.

If they were rubies
Glowing there,
We'd pluck a fortune
From the air,

But have no apples
Left to eat:
And oh, they are
So crisp and sweet!

Kathryn Jackson

If I Were an Apple

If I were an apple
  And grew on a tree,
I think I'd drop down
  On a nice boy like me.

I wouldn't stay there
  Giving nobody joy:
I'd fall down at once
  And say, "Eat me, my boy!"

Old Rhyme

4

The Apple Tree

I stood beneath the apple tree,
  The apples were so good to see;
Very high above my head
  I saw them shining round and red.

A robin sang a tiny song,
  And after I had waited long
A fairy in the apple tree
  Threw an apple down to me.

Rose Fyleman

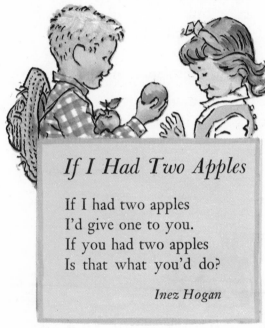

If I Had Two Apples

If I had two apples
I'd give one to you.
If you had two apples
Is that what you'd do?

Inez Hogan

Apple Pie

A was once an apple pie,
  Pidy,
  Widy,
  Tidy,
  Pidy,
  Nice insidy,
  Apple pie!

Edward Lear

Our Tree

When spring comes round, our apple tree
Is very full of flowers,
And when a bird sits on a branch
The petals fall in showers . . .

When summer comes our apple tree
Is very full of green,
And everywhere you look in it
There is a leafy screen.

When autumn comes our apple tree
Is full of things to eat.
The apples hang from every branch
To tumble at our feet.

When winter comes our apple tree
Is full of snow and ice,
And rabbits come to visit it . . .
We think our tree is nice.

Marchette Chute

A—Autumn

September

A road like brown ribbon,
A sky that is blue,
A forest of green
With the sky peeping through.

Asters, deep purple,
A grasshopper's call,
Today it is summer,
Tomorrow is fall.

Edwina Fallis

Gathering Gold

I walked through autumn woods today;
I cupped my hands along the way;
Great trees shook down rich coins of gold.
More than my two small hands could hold.

Katherine Edelman

Autumn Fires

In the other gardens
    And all up the vale,
From the autumn bonfires
    See the smoke trail!

Pleasant summer over
    And all the summer flowers,
The red fire blazes,
    The gray smoke towers.

Sing a song of seasons!
    Sometime bright in all!
Flowers in the summer,
    Fires in the fall!

Robert Louis Stevenson

Autumn Wind

Blow, wind—
    Blow the leaves along!
Blow, wind—
    Sing your little song!

Rattle all the red leaves,
    Shake them till they fall,
But make the brittle brown leaves
    Rattle best of all.

Blow, wind—
    Blow the leaves away
Sing a little song, wind,
    For an autumn day!

Helen Howland Prommel

6

Fall

The last of October
We close the garden gate.
(The flowers have all withered
That used to stand straight.)

The last of October
We put the swings away
And the porch looks deserted
Where we liked to play.

The last of October
The birds have all flown,
The screens are in the attic,
The sandpile's alone.

Everything is put away
Before it starts to snow . . .
I wonder if the ladybugs
Have any place to go?

Aileen Fisher

Autumn Song

These are the days of falling leaves,
The days of hazy weather,
Smelling of gold chrysanthemums
And gray wood-smoke together.

These are the nights of nearby stars,
The nights of closer moons,
When the windy darkness echoes
To crickets' farewell tunes.

Elizabeth-Ellen Long

November

Bracken on the hillside
frosted and white.
Garden all brown.
Storm windows tight.
Screens in the attic.
Barn full of hay.
Bathing suits mothproofed,
folded away.
And coming 'round the corner
on his tip, tip toes,
Winter, Winter, Winter
with a cold red nose!

Aileen Fisher

Autumn

The morns are meeker than they were,
    The nuts are getting brown;
The berry's cheek is plumper,
    The rose is out of town.

The maple wears a gayer scarf,
    The field a scarlet gown.
Lest I should be old-fashioned,
    I'll put a trinket on.

Emily Dickinson

 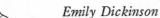

7

B—Balls and Balloons

Balls

Red balls.
Blue balls.
Big balls.
Little balls.
Throw them!
Roll them!
That is easy!

Red balls.
Blue balls.
Big balls.
Little balls.
Try to catch them!
That is hard!

Edith Osswald

Playing Ball

Ball, ball,
    Hit the wall,
Hurry back
    Before you fall.

Hurry back
    To me, and then
I will throw you
    Out again.

Marchette Chute

Balloons . . . Balloons

Balloons, balloons
    on colored string
    are blowing out
    into the Spring.

Balloons, balloons
    filled up with air
    are sailing off
    to everywhere.

Balloons, balloons
    all bright and round
    are floating up
    without a sound.

Myra Cohn Livingston

The Restless Balloon

Gay balloon,
Round and blue,
I should like
To fly with you.
Must you sail,
You pretty thing,
Where brave star fleets
Go voyaging?
Oh, don't tug so
At the string!

Rachel Field

8

B—Bears

Furry Bear

If I were a bear,
    And a big bear too,
I shouldn't much care
    If it froze or snew;
I shouldn't much mind
    If it snowed or friz—
I'd be all fur-lined
    With a coat like his!

For I'd have fur boots and a brown fur wrap,
And brown fur knickers and a big fur cap.
I'd have a fur muffle-ruff to cover my jaws,
And brown fur mittens on my big brown paws.
With a big brown furry-down up to my head,
I'd sleep all the winter in a big fur bed.

A. A. Milne

A Bear's Life

A Bear takes life quite easy
As a rule.
In Fall he just trots off to bed
Instead of school.

Orissa Rines

B Is for Bear

I like
Bears
And Lions
All right
And
Especially
In their
Cages
But
I like Bears
And Lions
The most
When
They're only
Just on
Pages.

Lysbeth Boyd Borie

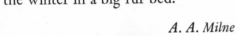

Little Brown Bear

Woof! Woof! Woof!
Brown bear—Yum!
Here is honey.
Come—eat some!

I know you like it
Because it's good—
Little brown bear,
Living in the wood.

Alice Wilkins

9

B—Birds

Robins

I wonder if the robins heard
That I would like to catch a bird,
For every robin seems to be
Just a bit afraid of me.

Romney Gay

Look at Six Eggs[1]

Look at six eggs
In a mockingbird's nest.

Listen to six mockingbirds
Flinging follies of O-be-joyful
Over the marshes and uplands.

Look at songs
Hidden in eggs.

Carl Sandburg

Four Little Birds

Four little birds all flew from their nests,—
Flew north, flew south, flew east and west;
They thought they would like a wider view,
So they spread their wings and away they flew.

Mary Mapes Dodge

Keep Off

Bird
Keep off the grass.
Don't you see the sign?
It says, PLEASE.

Jean Jászi

[1]This is an excerpt from a much longer poem by Carl Sandburg entitled "Prairie" from *Cornhuskers* by Carl Sandburg, copyright 1918 by Holt, Rinehart and Winston, Inc. Copyright renewed 1946 by Carl Sandburg. Reprinted by permission of Holt, Rinehart and Winston, Inc.

The Woodpecker

The woodpecker pecked out a little round hole
And made him a house in the telephone pole.

And one day when I watched he poked out his head,
And he had on a hood and a collar of red.

When the streams of rain pour out of the sky,
And the sparkles of lightning go flashing by,

And the big, big wheels of thunder roll,
He can snuggle back in the telephone pole.

Elizabeth Madox Roberts

No Shop Does the Bird Use

No shop does the bird use,
no counter nor baker,
but the bush is his orchard,
the grass is his acre,
the ant is his quarry,
the seed is his bread,
and a star is his candle
to light him to bed.

Elizabeth Coatsworth

How?

How do they know—
the robins and larks—
when it's time to return
to the meadows and parks?

How do they know
when the fall is still here
it's the "thing" to go south
that time of the year?

Do you think that a bird
is just smart, or, instead,
that he carries a calendar
'round in his head?

Aileen Fisher

11

B—Birthdays

A Birthday

Did you ever think how queer
That, every day all through the year,
Someone has a frosted cake,
And candles for a birthday's sake?

Rachel Field

The Party[1]

One day an invitation came,
It was addressed in my own name

And said a party there would be
And could I come Tuesday at three?

And Mother wrote and said I could
And made me promise to be good.

I licked the stamp, put on my coat
And all alone I mailed the note.

And then each morning I would say,
"Is this the birthday party day?"

Until my mother said it was
And I was very glad because

I wanted very much to go
(You know I do love ice cream so).

. . . .

I kissed my mother, reached the door
And she said, "Jimmy, one thing more

Now do be sure and be polite
Remember, shake hands with your RIGHT."

But all the time 'twas like a dream
('Cause I was thinking of ice cream).

Kate Cox Goddard

The Birthday Child

Everything's been different
    All the day long,
Lovely things have happened,
    Nothing has gone wrong.

Nobody has scolded me,
    Everyone has smiled.
Isn't it delicious
    To be a birthday child?

Rose Fyleman

Twins

They have the same birthday.
    Each looks like the other
'Cause one is a twin,
    And so is his brother!

Vivian G. Gouled

[1]From "The Party" by Kate Cox Goddard.

Open the Gift

The ribbons
Won't undo!
My fingers
Don't obey!
The paper's
Stubborn, too,
All sticking
In the way!

Regina Sauro

The Difference

I know that he is ten years old
And I am only eight;
But I can squeeze through the
    space beneath
The little back-yard gate.

Eleanor A. Chaffee

Seven Today

There's a book
with many pictures;
there are flowers
on slender stalks;
there's a little
string of seed-pearls,
and a doll
which sleeps and talks;
there's a tiny
perfume-bottle
as sweet-smelling
as can be;
there's a CAKE
with SEVEN CANDLES . . .
and they're all—for—ME!

Ivy O. Eastwick

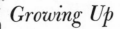

Growing Up

I'm wondering
If a boy
Just grows,
And grows,
And grows,
And grows,
Until he knows
As much as
        Father.

Vilate Raile

13

B—Boats

Boats

The steamboat is a slow poke,
 You simply cannot rush him.
The sailboat will not move at all
 Without a wind to push him;

But the speedboat, with his sharp red nose,
 Is quite a different kind;
He tosses high the spray, and leaves
 The other boats behind.

Rowena Bennett

Ferry Me Across the Water

"Ferry me across the water,
 Do, boatman, do."
"If you've a penny in your purse
 I'll ferry you."

"I have a penny in my purse,
 And my eyes are blue;
So ferry me across the water,
 Do, boatman, do!"

"Step into my ferry-boat,
 Be they black or blue,
And for the penny in your purse
 I'll ferry you."

Christina Rossetti

The Barge

I saw a great barge
 On the river today
All roomy and large,
 All painted and gay.
And only a boy
 And a dog were in charge . . .
Oh, think what a joy
 To look after a barge.

Rose Fyleman

Whistles

I never even hear
The boats that pass by day;
By night they seem so near,
A-whistling down the bay,
That I can almost understand
The things their whistles say.

I've waked sometimes all warm
In my bed, when eerily
I have heard them out of the dark
A-whistling cheerily
To tell the sleepy folk on land
All's well at sea.

Rachel Field

14

Boats

Vessels large may venture more,
But little boats should keep near shore.

Benjamin Franklin

15

B—Books

On Opening a New Book

Here's an adventure! What awaits
Beyond these closed, mysterious gates?
Whom shall I meet, where shall I go
Beyond the lovely land I know?
Above the sky, across the sea?
What shall I learn and feel and be?
Open, strange doors, to good or ill!
I hold my breath a moment still
Before the magic of your look.
What will you do to me, O Book?

Abbie Farwell Brown

B Was a Book

B was a book
With a binding of blue,
And pictures and stories
For me and for you.

B

Nice little book!

Edward Lear

Books

Some books are full of pictures,
Some books are very small,
Some books are thin and some are thick,
If I were asked to answer quick,
I'd say, "I like them all."

Romney Gay

16

After the End

After a book is finished,
Don't you wish you knew
Everything that happened
AFTER it was through?

Aileen Fisher

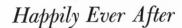

The Land of Storybooks

At evening when the lamp is lit,
Around the fire my parents sit;
They sit at home and talk and sing,
And do not play at anything.

Now, with my little gun, I crawl
All in the dark along the wall,
And follow round the forest track
Away behind the sofa back.

There, in the night, where none can spy,
All in my hunter's camp I lie,
And play at books that I have read
Till it is time to go to bed.

These are the hills, these are the woods,
These are my starry solitudes;
And there the river by whose brink
The roaring lions come to drink.

I see the others far away
As if in firelit camp they lay,
And I, like to an Indian scout,
Around their party prowled about.

So, when my nurse comes in for me,
Home I return across the sea,
And go to bed with backward looks
At my dear land of Storybooks.

Robert Louis Stevenson

Happily Ever After

Stories are
A joy to me—
Merry tales—all bright
With laughter.

But best of all
Are those that end:
"And they lived happily
Ever after!"

Ilo Orleans

My Book

My book and heart
Shall never part.

Old Rhyme

C—Christmas

For Christmas

Now not a window small or big
But wears a wreath or holly sprig;
Nor any shop too poor to show
Its spray of pine or mistletoe.

Now people hurry to and fro
With little girls and boys in tow,
And not a child but keeps some trace
Of Christmas secrets in his face.

Rachel Field

The Forest School

The little firs demurely stand
In studious rows, on either hand,
On winter days about like these,
All learning to be Christmas trees.

Mary Carolyn Davies

Do Not Open Until Christmas

I shake—shake,
Shake—shake,
Shake the package well.

But what there is
Inside of it,
Shaking will not tell.

James S. Tippett

Day Before Christmas

We have been helping with the cake
   And licking out the pan,
And wrapping up our packages
   As neatly as we can.
And we have hung our stockings up
   Beside the open grate,
And now there's nothing more to do
   Except
       To
           Wait!

Marchette Chute

Stay, Christmas!

Stay, Christmas!
Stay, Christmas!
Do not go
Away, Christmas.
Laughter jolly,
Lanterns, holly,
Bells ringing,
Children singing,
All things glad
Nothing sad . . .
Oh Stay, Christmas!
Stay, Christmas.
Do not go
Away, Christmas.

Ivy O. Eastwick

Wish on the Christmas Star

Star light,
Star bright,
Wonderful star
Of Christmas night,
I wish I may
I wish I might
Have the wish
I wish tonight:

*Christmas peace,
Christmas joys—
For all God's world
Of girls and boys.*

Marion Doyle

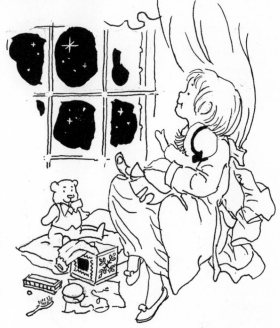

The Day After Christmas

The day after Christmas
Friend on young friend calls.
All the happy girls are out
Showing off their dolls!

The day after Christmas,
Mid noisy shouts and squeals,
All the happy boys are out
Riding things on wheels!

The day after Christmas,
Ere winter twilight falls,
All the frisky dogs are out
Chasing brand-new balls!

Decie Merwin

19

Circus Day

The circus is here!
   It came in the night:
Ladies in spangles,
   And clowns in white;
Tigers and lions
   Fiercely bright,
Every sort of a
   Smell and sight.

And they say a boy can
   earn a quarter
Bringing the elephants
   pails of water!

Rachel Field

C—The Circus

Bare-Back Rider

There isn't a prettier sight, I think,
Than a pony that's white and a lady that's pink:
The pony so frisky and stepping so high,
The lady so smiling as they go by,
The lady so tiptoe on her toes,
The pony, his bridle dressed up with a rose,
The lady and pony both liking to be
Riding around for the world to see.

Dorothy Aldis

The Acrobats

Flying high on silver bars
Ladies spangled like the sun
Turn just so, and then let go—
And catch another one!
And smile when they come down, and wave,
And are not proud of being brave.

Dorothy Aldis

20

I Want to Be a Clown

I went to see the Circus
(Last week it was in town).
So now at home I'm practicing
To be a funny clown.

Romney Gay

The Circus Clown and the Circus Horse

Said the circus clown to the circus horse,
"I'm going to ride on your back, of course."

Said the circus horse to the circus clown,
"Take care that you do not tumble down!"

Just then the horse began to stumble,
And the circus clown began to tumble.

But nobody cared a bit, you know;
It was only a part of the circus show!

Carolyn Forsyth

There'll Be a Clown

The circus is coming to town once more!
    The circus is coming to town!
There'll be tigers in cages, a lion that rages,
    And there'll be a clown, a clown!
There'll be a clown with a suit of white,
Striped in green and purple bright,
With a wide, wide grin he laughs each night,
A clown to tumble, and grumble, and fight,
    When the circus comes to town!

Mary Carolyn Davies

21

C—The City

Buildings

Buildings are a great surprise,
Every one's a different size.

Offices
grow
long
and
high,
tall
enough
to
touch
the
sky.

Houses seem
more like a box,
made of glue
and building blocks.

Every time you look, you see
buildings shaped quite differently.

Myra Cohn Livingston

Trip to the City

I'm taking a trip to the city
I'll ride on the subway and such,
I have to be careful in traffic
But I do like the city so much.

I like to look up at the buildings
The windows shine wonderfully bright;
I always stay up a bit later
The city's so pretty at night.

Kate Cox Goddard

Fourth Floor!

"Fourth floor!"
Is what I say
When I come in
From play.

My home
Is on that floor.
It has a seven
On the door.

Six other doors
Are on our hall
With a different family
Behind them all.

James S. Tippett

City Song

Many windows,
many floors,
many people,
many stores,
many streets
and many bangings,
many whistles,
many clangings
many, many, many, many—
many of everything, many of any!

James Steel Smith

When You Walk

When you walk in a field,
Look down
Lest you trample
A daisy's crown!

But in a city
Look always high,
And watch
The beautiful clouds go by!

James Stephens

City Lights

Into the endless dark
The lights of the buildings shine,
Row upon twinkling row,
Line upon glistening line.
Up and up they mount
Till the tallest seems to be
The topmost taper set
On a towering Christmas tree.

Rachel Field

In the City

Do you live in a city, high, high from the ground
And look out of your window—up, down, and around?
Up higher than you is a piece of blue sky,
Down lower than you are things whizzing by,
All around you are buildings, low and tall,
With windows and windows, or a big blank wall.
But just look across, you'll see someone who
Looks straight across, too, and right back at you.

Zhenya Gay

23

C—The Country

Country Pathway

I walked a country pathway—
    It led now east, now west;
I found a clover meadow
    And threw me down to rest.

I saw a purple butterfly,
    I saw some golden bees,
I saw some dancing shadows
    Cast by two tall elm trees.

I walked back hours later,
    And, still about my head,
I smelled the rosy-cozy smell
    That marks a clover bed!

R. A. Stevens

The Pasture

I'm going out to clean the pasture spring;
I'll only stop to rake the leaves away
(And wait to watch the water clear, I may):
I sha'n't be gone long. —You come too.

I'm going out to fetch the little calf
That's standing by the mother. It's so young
It totters when she licks it with her tongue.
I sha'n't be gone long. —You come too.

Robert Frost

In the Country

Ate an apple,
ate a pear,
saw a tractor,
rode a mare,
spied a possum,
heard larks sing—
Oh, I went walking
to the spring.

James Steel Smith

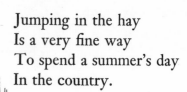

Hayloft

Jumping in the hay
Is a very fine way
To spend a summer's day
In the country.

Jean Jászi

In the Country

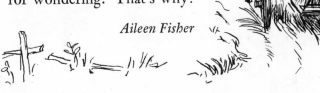

I think people wonder
in the country much more
than they wonder in the city
with houses next door:

They see more world
in the country, more sky,
so there's much more space
for wondering. That's why!

Aileen Fisher

City Streets and Country Roads

The city has streets—
    But the country has roads.
In the country one meets
    Blue carts with their loads
Of sweet-smelling hay,
    And mangolds, and grain:
Oh, take me away
    To the country again!

In the city one sees,
    Big trams rattle by,
And the breath of the chimneys
    That blot out the sky,
And all down the pavements
    Stiff lampposts one sees—
But the country has hedgerows,
    The country has trees.

As sweet as the sun
    In the country is rain:
Oh, take me away
    To the country again!

Eleanor Farjeon

Plans

If I'd a little money
    I wouldn't travel far,
I wouldn't buy an aeroplane,
    I wouldn't buy a car.

I'd buy a weeny cottage
    Among the Wiltshire downs,
With a garden full of flowers
    That will not grow in towns.

I'd buy the prettiest basket
    That ever I could see,
And fill it up with blackberries
    And bring them back for tea.

And from the village grocer
    Buy honey in the comb,
And spend a little money
    On my little country home.

Luisa Hewitt

A Country Child's Prayer

Bless our sowing,
Bless our reaping.
Bless our waking,
Bless our sleeping.
Bless our working,
Bless our playing.
Hear us, Lord,
And bless our praying.

Ivy O. Eastwick

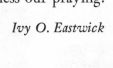

Cowboy Hats

When we went to the market
with our mother and her money,
we had to wear our cowboy hats
because the day was sunny.

When we went to our neighbors,
to their rubber pool for wading,
we had to wear our cowboy hats
to give the pool a shading.

When we went through the drizzle
and the mist to see Aunt Ella,
we had to wear our cowboy hats . . .
instead of an umbrella.

Aileen Fisher

C—Cowboys

High Top Boots

I've a track and engine,
  The whistle loudly toots!
I've a bow and arrow
  The kind an Indian shoots!
My moccasins are beaded,
  And I've two Indian suits!
But I have something finer,
  A pair of *high top boots!*
Trains and tracks are dandy,
  And so's a bow that shoots!
Moccasins are handy,
  And so are Indian suits!
I like trains with whistles,
  The kind that loudly toots,
But there is nothing finer
  Than *shiny high top boots!*

Nona Keen Duffy

Cowboy Song

Mount your brave pinto
  And we'll travel west.
That is the life
  That a cowboy likes best.
Far from the bunkhouse
  We'll gallop away
Singing, "Yip-pee-ki!
  Yip-pee-ki! Yip-pee-ki-yay!"

We'll cook by a campfire,
  And spread out our bed.
We'll sleep on the ground
  With the sky for a spread.
Far from the ranch house,
  Where antelopes play,
We'll hear wild coyotes
  Before it is day.
We'll whirl our long ropes
  And here's what we'll say,
"Yip-pee-ki! Yip-pee-ki!
  Yip-pee-ki-yay!"

Nona Keen Duffy

26

The Rodeo

One day my Daddy took me
To the Rodeo;
We climbed up in the grandstand
And waited for the show.

The cowboys all looked dandy,
In green and yellow shirts;
Their hats were called "John Stetsons,"
And they carried riding quirts.

They rode fierce, bucking horses!
They twirled their lariats too—
They roped and tied the wriggling calves;
And yelled when they were through.

Soon all the fun was over,
The cowboys left the ring;
They shouted as they rode away—
"We'll see you all next Spring!"

Cathryn Green

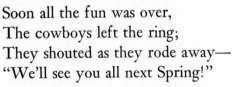

The Cowboy's Life

The rapid beat
Of his broncho's feet
    On the sod as he speeds along,
Keeps living time
To the ringing rhyme
    Of his rollicking cowboy song.

The winds may blow
And the thunder growl
    Or the breezes may safely moan;—
A cowboy's life
Is a royal life
    His saddle his kingly throne.

John A. Lomax

27

D—Dogs

D Is for Dog

Says the prancing French poodle
As he trots with the band
When it plays "Yankee Doodle":
"Bow-wow! I hate CATS—
The whole kit-and-caboodle!"

William Jay Smith

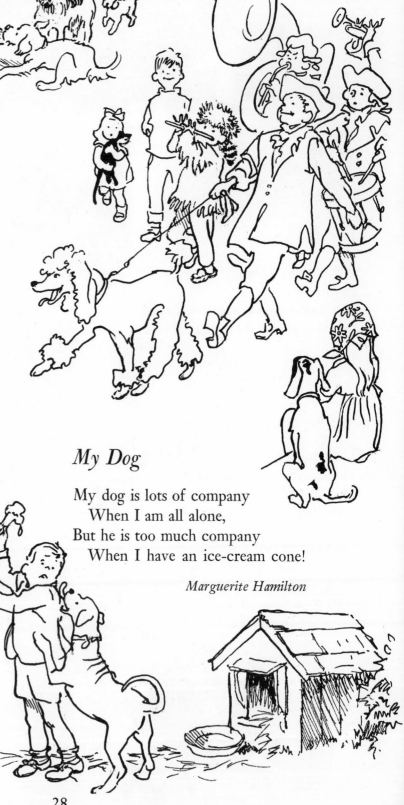

The Welcome

Always when we come indoors
He's waiting, small and black,
Wagging and wiggle-ing about,
So happy that we're back.

He races up and down the hall.
He snorts. He barks out loud.
And then he runs to get his ball
And shows it to us—Proud.

Dorothy Aldis

My Dog

My dog is lots of company
    When I am all alone,
But he is too much company
    When I have an ice-cream cone!

Marguerite Hamilton

28

Quack!

The duck is whiter than whey is,
His tail tips up over his back,
The eye in his head is as round as a button,
And he says, *Quack! Quack!*

He swims on his bright blue mill-pond,
By the willow tree under the shack,
Then stands on his head to see down to the bottom,
And says, *Quack! Quack!*

When Mollie steps out of the kitchen,
For apron—pinned round with a sack;
He squints at her round face, her dish, and what's in it,
And says, *Quack! Quack!*

He preens the pure snow of his feathers
In the sun by the wheat-straw stack;
At dusk waddles home with his brothers and sisters,
And says, *Quack! Quack!*

Walter de la Mare

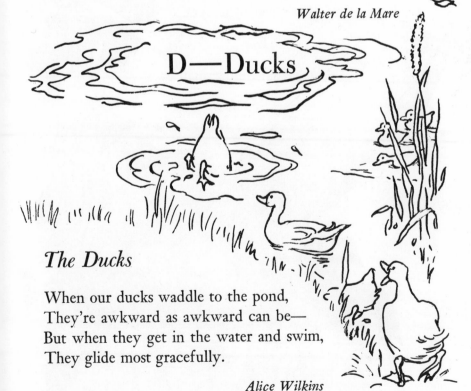

The Ducks

When our ducks waddle to the pond,
They're awkward as awkward can be—
But when they get in the water and swim,
They glide most gracefully.

Alice Wilkins

D Was a Duck

D was a duck
With spots on his back,
Who lived in the water,
And always said, "Quack!"

D

Dear little duck!

Edward Lear

Railroad Ducks

Five ducks in the pond
By the railroad track
Rejoice whenever
A train roars by.
They bob and stretch
Their wings and quack,
While children in
The train all cry,

"Look at the ducks!"
And the ducks with pride
Splash and kick up
A fine commotion.
In the wake of the train
They gently ride
The little waves
Of their private ocean.

Frances Frost

29

E—Elephants

Pet Elephant

I'd like to own an elephant.
I'd love him at first glance,
For waggly trunk and floppy ears
And baggy-kneed gray pants.

Marjorie Abbott

E Was an Elephant

E was an elephant,
Stately and wise:
He had tusks and a trunk,
And two queer little eyes.

E

Oh, what funny small eyes!

Edward Lear

How They Walk

When elephants walk,
They walk like this:
Clump—clump—clump.
They're very heavy and very slow.
This is the way that elephants go:
Clump—clump—clump.

When kitty-cats walk
They walk like this:
Pitpat—pitpat—pitpat.
They're soft as silk and elegant—
Not at all like an elephant.
Pitpat—pitpat—pitpat.

Grace Olin Jordan

The Elephant

When people call this beast to mind,
They marvel more and more
At such a *little* tail behind,
So LARGE a trunk before.

Hilaire Belloc

Louella the Elephant

I know a wooly elephant,
Her name is Miss Louella.
When it rains and sloshes,
She wears galoshes
And carries a beach umbrella.

Ethel Jacobson

Holding Hands

Elephants walking
Along the trails
Are holding hands
By holding tails.

Trunks and tails
Are handy things
When elephants walk
In circus rings.

Elephants work
And elephants play
And elephants walk
And feel so gay.

And when they walk—
It never fails
They're holding hands
By holding tails.

Lenore Link

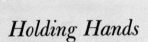

An Elephant

An elephant has an awfully long nose
And looks as if he'd slept in his clothes.

Zhenya Gay

E—Elevators · Escalators

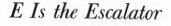

E Is the Escalator

E is the Escalator
   That gives an elegant ride.
You step on the stair
With an easy air
   And up and up you glide.
It's nicer than scaling ladders
   Or scrambling 'round a hill,
For you climb and climb
But all the time,
   You're really standing still.

Phyllis McGinley

The Elevator

The elevator
In the store
Has a door
That slides
Open—closed.

Then the driver moves a handle,
And up and up
The elevator slips
And *stops*
And *out* go some people
And *in* come some people.

And up and up the elevator slips
And stops
And out go some people
And in come some people.
And down and *down*
The elevator drops
   To the floor
   Where I
   Get out.

Dorothy W. Baruch

Moving Stairs

I love to ride the magic stair,
It doesn't cost a penny fare.
I stand quite still, and up it goes,
Walking while I rest my toes.
I get off at the top, a second before
My step runs underneath the floor.

Ida M. Pardue

Fairies

Don't go looking for fairies,
    They'll fly away if you do.
You never can see the fairies
    Till they come looking for you.

Eleanor Farjeon

F—Fairies

Some One

Some one came knocking
    At my wee, small door;
Some one came knocking,
    I'm sure—sure—sure;
I listened, I opened,
    I looked to left and right,
But nought there was a-stirring
    In the still dark night;
Only the busy beetle
    Tap-tapping in the wall,
Only from the forest
    The screech-owl's call,
Only the cricket whistling
    While the dewdrops fall,
So I know not who came knocking,
    At all, at all, at all.

Walter de la Mare

As You Would Be Done By

Of course I believe in fairies!
    Of course I know they're true!
—Just think, if you were a fairy,
    And no one believed in you!

Mary Carolyn Davies

Our Baby

Our baby came home
With Daddy and Mother
And I came along
To be his brother,
    And now
    We are four
    At the door
    For each other.

Myra Cohn Livingston

Portrait

Always in a hurry,
    Always on the go—
That's my little sister.
    Don't I know!

Marchette Chute

Walking

When Daddy
Walks
With Jean and me,
We have a
Lot of fun
'Cause we can't
Walk as fast
As he,
Unless we
Skip and
Run.
I stretch,
And stretch
My legs so far,
I nearly slip
And fall—
But how
Does Daddy
Take such steps?
He doesn't stretch
At all!

Grace Ellen Glaubitz

F—The Family

Comparison

John is the tallest—he's ever so high;
Betty's a little bit taller than I;
I'm not as tall as Betty is tall;
But John is the tallest, the tallest of all.
    Tall, taller, tallest,
    One, two, and three.
    Both John and Betty
    Stretch high over me.
But turn it around and it's better for me
Because I'm the shortest of all the three.
    Short, shorter, shortest,
    Hello and good-by.
    I am the shortest;
    The shortest am I.

Mary Ann Hoberman

Let's Be Merry

Mother shake the cherry tree,
    Susan catch a cherry;
Oh, how funny that will be,
    Let's be merry!

One for brother, one for sister,
    Two for mother more,
Six for father, hot and tired,
    Knocking at the door.

Christina Rossetti

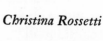

34

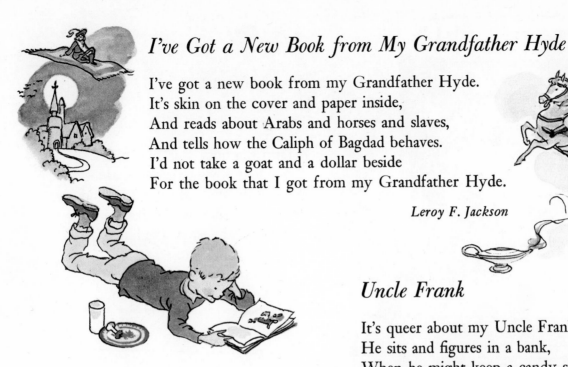

I've Got a New Book from My Grandfather Hyde

I've got a new book from my Grandfather Hyde.
It's skin on the cover and paper inside,
And reads about Arabs and horses and slaves,
And tells how the Caliph of Bagdad behaves.
I'd not take a goat and a dollar beside
For the book that I got from my Grandfather Hyde.

Leroy F. Jackson

Uncle Frank

It's queer about my Uncle Frank,
He sits and figures in a bank,
When he might keep a candy store—
A shining sign above the door.
Or he might keep a big toy shop
With things that fly and skip and hop—
With trailer trucks and things that crank,
Instead of working in a bank.

Monica Shannon

The Cupboard

I know a little cupboard,
With a teeny tiny key,
And there's a jar of Lollipops
  For me, me, me.

It has a little shelf, my dear,
As dark as dark can be,
And there's a dish of Banbury Cakes
  For me, me, me.

I have a small fat grandmamma,
With a very slippery knee,
And she's Keeper of the Cupboard
  With the key, key, key.

And when I'm very good, my dear,
As good as good can be,
There's Banbury Cakes, and Lollipops
  For me, me, me.

Walter de la Mare

35

F—The Farm

What Is a Farm?

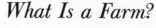

What is a farm?
O what is a farm
That lies in the lee of the hill?

A farm is a busy working thing,
A cackling, lowing, growing thing
Where rain and sun make live things grow
Where farmers sow and reap and mow
  There in the lee of the hill.

Lucy Sprague Mitchell

The Cow

The friendly cow all red and white,
I love with all my heart:
She gives me cream with all her might,
To eat with apple tart.

She wanders lowing here and there,
And yet she cannot stray,
All in the pleasant open air,
The pleasant light of day;

And blown by all the winds that pass
And wet with all the showers,
She walks among the meadow grass
And eats the meadow flowers.

Robert Louis Stevenson

Cleverness

I can bridle a horse,
  Or milk a cow,
Or dig potatoes,
  Or guide a plow,
Or call the chickens
  And make them come—
If someone's around
  To help me some.

Marchette Chute

Chicks

As soon as chicks pop out of eggs,
They run around on their *own* two legs!

Ilo Orleans

Trouble at the Farm

Help! Help!
What's to do?
Dobbin, the horse
Has cast a shoe!

Help! Help!
What is the matter?
Porkie, the pig
Has eaten the platter!

Help! Help!
What is it now?
Sammie, the sheepdog
Is chasing the cow!

Oh! dear!
What a to-do!
Such muddles and troubles
I never knew!

Ivy O. Eastwick

The Barnyard

When the Farmer's day is done,
In the barnyard, ev'ry one,
Beast and bird politely say,
"Thank you for my food today."

The cow says, "Moo!"
The pigeon, "Coo!"
The sheep say, "Baa!"
The lamb says, "Maa!"
The hen, "Cluck, Cluck!"
"Quack!" says the duck;
The dog, "Bow Wow!"
The cat, "Meow!"
The horse says, "Neigh!
I love sweet hay!"
The pig nearby,
Grunts in his sty.

When the barn is locked up tight
Then the Farmer says, "Good-night!"
Thanks his animals ev'ry one,
For the work that has been done.

Maud Burnham

37

F—Flowers

The Forsythia Bush

The forsythia bush, as everyone knows,
Is sunshine arranged in bright little bows;
You never would dream it could do such a trick!
At just the right moment, it bursts through the stick,
The earliest, curliest feather of spring,
Like clouds of canaries, intending to sing.
But whether they sing or just hold on tight,
The forsythia bush is a musical sight.

Miriam Clark Potter

A Spike of Green

When I went out
The sun was hot,
It shone upon
My flower pot.

And there I saw
A spike of green
That no one else
Had ever seen!

On other days
The things I see
Are mostly old
Except for me.

But this green spike
So new and small
Had never yet
Been seen at all!

Barbara Baker

Maytime Magic

A little seed
For me to sow . . .

A little earth
To make it grow . . .
A little hole,
A little pat . . .
A little wish,
And that is that.

A little sun,
A little shower . . .
A little while,
And then—a flower!

Mabel Watts

Dandelions

When dandelions are yellow,
I make a chain of gold.
But I love to blow their heads off
When dandelions are old.

Romney Gay

38

Daisies

Where innocent bright-eyed daisies are,
  With blades of grass between,
Each daisy stands up like a star
  Out of a sky of green.

Christina Rossetti

Nosegay

Violets, daffodils,
  roses and thorn
were all in the garden
  before you were born.

Daffodils, violets,
  red and white roses
your grandchildren's children
  will hold to their noses.

Elizabeth Coatsworth

Picking Flowers

Flowers here, flowers there,
Flowers growing everywhere.
Though I pick and pick and pick,
Still they seem to be quite thick.

Romney Gay

Relatives

Sunflower so big!
Brown-eyed Susan so small!
You look so much alike,
You ought to be related
If flowers can be relatives at all.

Tom Robinson

Names

Larkspur and Hollyhock,
Pink Rose and purple Stock,
Lovely smelling Mignonette,
Lilies not quite opened yet,
Phlox the favorite of bees,
Bleeding Heart and Peonies—
Just their names are nice to say,
Softly,
On a summer's day.

Dorothy Aldis

F—Funny Things

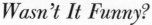

Wasn't It Funny?

Wasn't it funny, hear it,
    all people!
Little Tom Thumb has swallowed
    a steeple!

How did he do it?
I'll tell you my son!
'Twas made of white sugar—and
    easily done!

Old Rhyme

If You Ever

If you ever ever ever ever ever
If you ever ever ever meet a whale
You must never never never never never
You must never never never touch its tail:
For if you ever ever ever ever ever,
If you ever ever ever touch its tail,
You will never, never, never, never, never,
You will never never meet another whale.

Author Unknown

Funny

When you stop to think of it, isn't it funny—
the wiggle-y nose that there is on a bunny,
the smartness of bees to know all about honey,
the difference in days that are rainy or sunny,
the way that our legs can be walky or runny,
the things you can buy, if you just have the money—
When you stop to think of it, isn't it funny?

Aileen Fisher

The Neck

The neck
Of a calf
    Is a half
    Of a half
    Of a half
    Of a half
    Of a half
    Of a half
    Of a half
    Of a half
Of the size
Of the neck
Of a little
Giraffe.

Ilo Orleans

The Funniest Thing

What's the funniest thing you can think of?
What's the funniest thing you can think of?
A monkey doing tricks?
A house built out of sticks?
An elephant juggling bricks?
What's the funniest thing *you* can think of?

Beatrice Schenk de Regniers

Wouldn't It Be Funny?

Wouldn't it be funny—
Wouldn't it now,—
If the dog said, "Moo-oo"
And the cat said, "Bow-wow"?
If the cat sang and whistled,
And the bird said, "Mia-ow"?
Wouldn't it be funny—
Wouldn't it now?

Old Rhyme

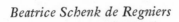

Tip-Toe Tale

A fish took a notion
To come from his ocean
And take in the sights of the town.
So he bought him a hat
And a coat and cravat
And a one legg-ed trouser of brown! *He did!*
A one legg-ed trouser of brown!

His suit fit so queerly
That everyone nearly
Went following out on the street!
But the best of it all
Was how handsome and tall
He could walk when he didn't have feet! *He did!*
He walked when he didn't have feet!

Now I must confess that
I surely could guess that
A fish trying walking would fail
But with no one's advice
He walked *perfectly* nice
On the very tip-toes of his tail! *He did!*
On the very tip-toes of his tail!

Dixie Willson

The Funny Fly

"Ho!" buzzed the housefly,
"I'm *such* a clown!"
And he walked on the ceiling
Upside down.

Mabel Watts

41

G—Gardens

Gardening Is Heaps of Fun!

Gardening is heaps of fun!
We are partners with the sun,
For we help him make things grow,
With our spade and rake and hoe!

Mary Carolyn Davies

In the Garden

It's good to be back
  At the soil again,
Out in the garden
  To toil again.

It's good to plant
  And to sow again,
To dig and to rake
  And to hoe again.

I'm happy and merry:
  I sing again,
Because today
  It is spring again.

Ilo Orleans

Gardening

I think my garden's small
Till I begin to dig,
And then before I'm through,
I think it's VERY big.

Anne Zuker

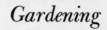

Seeds

The seeds I sowed—
For weeks unseen—
Have pushed up pygmy
Shoots of green;
So frail you'd think
The tiniest stone
Would never let
A glimpse be shown.

But no; a pebble
Near them lies,
At least a cherry-stone
In size,
Which that mere sprout
Has heaved away,
To bask in sunshine,
See the Day.

Walter de la Mare

42

Five Little Marigolds

Five little marigolds standing in a row;
Now isn't that the best way for marigolds to grow?
Each with a green stalk, and all the five had got
A bright yellow flower, and a new red pot.

Kate Greenaway

Vegetables

A carrot has a green fringed top;
   A beet is royal red;
And lettuces are curious
   All curled and run to head.

Some beans have strings to tie them on,
   And, what is still more queer,
Ripe corn is nothing more or less
   Than one enormous ear!

But when potatoes all have eyes,
   Why is it they should be
Put in the ground and covered up—
   Where it's too dark to see?

Rachel Field

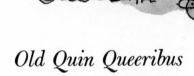

Old Quin Queeribus

Old Quin Queeribus—
   He loved his garden so,
He wouldn't have a rake around,
   A shovel or a hoe.

For each potato's eyes he bought
   Fine spectacles of gold,
And mufflers for the corn to keep
   Its ears from getting cold.

On every head of lettuce green—
   What do you think of that?—
And every head of cabbage, too,
   He tied a garden hat.

Old Quin Queeribus—
   He loved his garden so,
He couldn't eat his growing things,
   He only let them grow!

Nancy Byrd Turner

The Tinkling Gate

Our neighbor has a tinkling gate
(I wish we had one too).

It makes me think of Valentines,
The kind I'd send to you.

Red roses climb along the fence
They hide the yard inside,

But once I walked by slowly when
The gate stood open wide.

A lady with her knitting sat
A-rocking near her door.

She seemed so very friendly that
I looked around once more.

Now we had just moved on that street
I didn't know her name,

But when she beckoned me to come
I went in just the same.

G—A Gate

She visited a minute, then
Gave me a lollipop

And told me next time that I passed
I must be sure to stop.

She said she knew my mother
And knew my daddy, so

I felt we were acquainted, but
Said, "I have to go."

I thanked her for the lollipop
(I tried to make it last),

I listened to the little gate
It tinkled as I passed.

Kate Cox Goddard

44

The Three Horses

Three horses came
to the meadow's edge—
they poked their noses
over the hedge.

One was gray,
one was white,
and one was black
as a winter's night.

I patted the white horse,
I stroked the gray,
and I rode the black horse
far away.

We went by the wood,
we went by the hill,
we galloped along
by Medlicott Mill.

Oh! if my mother
should question you—
I may be back
in an hour or two.

Ivy O. Eastwick

H—Horses

The Horse

With long-lashed eyes, both sad and wise,
    He looks at me intently.
His face is clean, and smooth and lean—
    He lets me stroke it gently.

Barbara Schaeffer

Work Horses

Big strong work horses working every day,
Big strong work horses pulling loads of hay,
Big strong work horses have no time to play,
    Work!—Work!—Work!
Big strong work horses with a wagon full,
Big strong work horses, pull! pull! pull!
    Pull!—Pull!—Pull!

    Big horse, strong horse,
    Pull the plow, pull the plow,
    Pull hard, work hard,
    Plow the garden, plow, plow!
    Big horse, tired horse,
    Stop and rest now.

Big strong work horses plowing up the ground,
Big strong work horses walking round and round,
Big strong work horses going home to lunch,
Eating oats, eating hay, munch! munch! munch!

Edith H. Newlin

Houses

How could God think of so many kinds of houses?
There are millions of houses that I can't even see.
There must be lots of very funny ones!
  Mole houses—
    Frog houses—
      Beaver houses—
Stork nests on chimneys,
Squirrel nests in trees.
Houses for everyone!
  And my house
    For me.

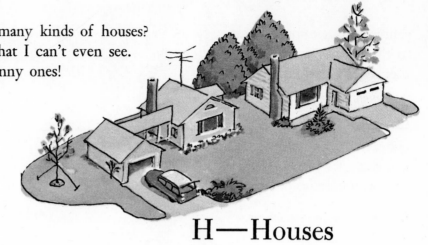

H—Houses

Jessie Orton Jones

The House at the Corner

The house at the corner
is cold gray stone,
where the trees and windows
crack and groan,
so I run past
          fast
            when I'm all alone.

Myra Cohn Livingston

The Unfinished House

Rooms without their doors in,
Stairs we cannot climb—
We like a house not finished yet.
We go there all the time.

But who is going to live here?
That's what we think about:
Will there be children's faces at
The windows looking out?

Dorothy Aldis

46

Song for a Little House

I'm glad our house is a little house,
  Not too tall nor too wide:
I'm glad the hovering butterflies
  Feel free to come inside.

Our little house is a friendly house,
  It is not shy or vain;
It gossips with the talking trees,
  And makes friends with the rain.

And quick leaves cast a shimmer of green
  Against our whited walls,
And in the phlox, the courteous bees
  Are paying duty calls.

Christopher Morley

My Houses

If I'd be a painter,
Here's just what I'd do:
I'd paint all the houses
Red, yellow, and blue.
The steps would be purple,
The roofs . . . pink and white,
And people would look at
My houses all right!

Vivian G. Gouled

Old Log House

On a little green knoll
At the edge of the wood
My great great grandmother's
First house stood.

The house was of logs
My grandmother said
With one big room
And a lean-to shed.

The logs were cut
And the house was raised
By pioneer men
In the olden days.

I like to hear
My grandmother tell
How they built the fireplace
And dug the well.

They split the shingles;
They filled each chink;
It's a house of which
I like to think.

Forever and ever
I wish I could
Live in a house
At the edge of a wood.

James S. Tippett

47

I—Indians

Little Papoose

Little papoose
Swung high in the branches
Hears a song of birds, stars, clouds,
Small nests of birds,
Small buds of flowers.
But he is thinking of his mother with dark hair
Like her horse's mane.

Fair clouds nod to him
Where he swings in the tree,
But he is thinking of his father
Dark and glistening and wonderful,

Of his father with a voice like ice and velvet,
And tones of falling water,
Of his father who shouts
Like a storm.

Hilda Conkling

Hiawatha's Childhood

Then the little Hiawatha
Learned of every bird its language,
Learned their names and all their secrets:
How they built their nests in Summer,
Where they hid themselves in Winter,
Talked with them whene'er he met them,
Called them "Hiawatha's Chickens."

Henry Wadsworth Longfellow

48

Indian Children

Where we walk to school each day
Indian children used to play—
All about our native land,
Where the shops and houses stand.

And the trees were very tall,
And there were no streets at all,
Not a church and not a steeple—
Only woods and Indian people.

Only wigwams on the ground,
And at night bears prowling round—
What a different place today
Where we live and work and play!

Annette Wynne

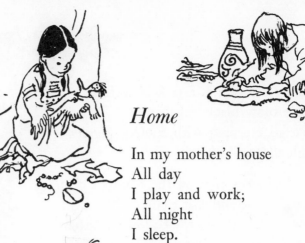

Home

In my mother's house
All day
I play and work;
All night
I sleep.

The walls come close around me
In a good way.
I can see them;
I can feel them;
I live with them.

This house is good to me,
It keeps me;
I like it,
My mother's house.

Ann Nolan Clark

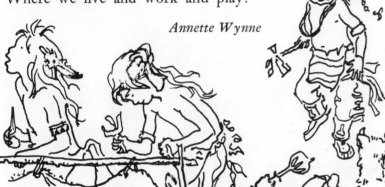

Ten Little Indians

One little, two little,
Three little Indians;
Four little, five little,
Six little Indians;
Seven little, eight little,
Nine little Indians,
Ten little Indian boys.

Old Rhyme

49

Halloween

The moon is round as a jack-o'-lantern;
The trees blow black and bare;
And we go creeping with spooky giggles
Through the chill ghostly air.

Whose shadow is that on the haunted ground?
Who's hiding behind that tree?
Oh, down the tree runs my bad black kitten,
And the shadow is only me!

Frances Frost

I Wonder Why

I don't know why it is, but I
Can't make a face that's scary;
I persevere—yet every year,
My jack-o'-lantern's merry!

Ida M. Pardue

J—Jack-O'-Lanterns

Halloween

Jack-o'-lantern in the dark,
You're a scare-y fellow,
Grinning mouth and shiny eyes,
Blinking, round and yellow.
I should be afraid I know—
If I hadn't watched you grow!

Rachel Field

J—Jumping

Jumping Rope

Jump with two feet,
Jump with one;
Either way is
Lots of fun.

Romney Gay

Jumping Joan

Here am I,
Little Jumping Joan;
When nobody's with me
I'm all alone.

Hinx, minx! the old witch winks,
The fat begins to fry;
There's nobody at home but Jumping Joan,
Father, Mother, and I!

Old Rhyme

Jumps

One jump, we'll jump to the moon,
Two jumps, we'll jump to a star—
Three and four and one or two more
And we shan't know where we are!

Rose Fyleman

51

The Duck and the Kangaroo

K—The Kangaroo

-1-

Said the Duck to the Kangaroo,
  "Good gracious! how you hop
Over the fields, and the water too,
  As if you never would stop!
My life is a bore in this nasty pond;
And I long to go out in the world beyond:
  I wish I could hop like you,"
  Said the Duck to the Kangaroo.

-2-

"Please give me a ride on your back,"
  Said the Duck to the Kangaroo:
"I would sit quite still, and say nothing but
    'Quack,'
  The whole of the long day through;
And we'd go the Dee, and the Jelly Bo Lee,
Over the land, and over the sea:
  Please take me a ride! oh, do!"
  Said the Duck to the Kangaroo.

-3-

Said the Kangaroo to the Duck,
  "This requires some little reflection.
Perhaps, on the whole, it might bring me
    luck:
  And there seems but one objection;
Which is, if you'll let me speak so bold,
Your feet are unpleasantly wet and cold,
  And would probably give me the roo—
  Matiz," said the Kangaroo.

-4-

Said the Duck, "As I sat on the rocks,
  I have thought over that completely;
And I bought four pairs of worsted socks,
  Which fit my web-feet neatly;
And, to keep out the cold, I've bought a
    cloak;
And every day a cigar I'll smoke;
  All to follow my own dear true
  Love of a Kangaroo."

-5-

Said the Kangaroo, "I'm ready,
  All in the moonlight pale;
But to balance me well, dear Duck, sit steady,
  And quite at the end of my tail."
So away they went with a hop and a bound;
And they hopped the whole world three times
    round.
  And who so happy, oh! who,
  As the Duck and the Kangaroo?

Edward Lear

52

K Was a Kite

K was a kite
Which flew out of sight,
Above houses so high,
Quite into the sky.

K

Fly away, kite!

Edward Lear

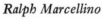

K—Kites

The Kite

A kite is never just a kite.
  It's a pennant that a boy
Sends up by means of string and wind
  To advertise his joy.

Ralph Marcellino

Kite Song

I am a kite high in the sky,
Floating along with the wind,
And the funniest thing . . .
I'm holding a string,
With a boy on the other end!

Avan Collum

A Kite

I often sit and wish that I
Could be a kite up in the sky,
And ride upon the breeze and go
Whichever way I chanced to blow.

Author Unknown

The Kite

How bright on the blue
Is a kite when it's new!

With a dive and a dip
It snaps its tail

Then soars like a ship
With only a sail

As over tides
Of wind it rides,

Climbs to the crest
Of a gust and pulls,

Then seems to rest
As wind falls.

When string goes slack
You wind it back

And run until
A new breeze blows

And its wings fill
And up it goes!

How bright on the blue
Is a kite when it's new!

But a raggeder thing
You never will see

When it flaps on a string
In the top of a tree.

Harry Behn

K—Kittens

A Thought

It's very nice to think of how
In every country lives a Cow
To furnish milk with all her might
For Kittens' comfort and delight.

Oliver Herford

The Kitten

The trouble with a kitten is
THAT
Eventually it becomes a
CAT.

Ogden Nash

New Kittens

We had one cat
And that was that;
And then today
While at our play
We heard a mew,
And there were two
Small baby kits.
Their eyes were slits
Not opened quite
To any light.
Their bodies were
Round balls of fur,
Their tiny tails
Were up like sails,
Their tongues were pink,
And oh, I think
They are so sweet,
Those balls with feet!

Grace Noll Crowell

Pussy Feet

My kitty makes
No noise because
She walks around
On velvet paws.

Ruth Chandler

I Held a Lamb

One day when I went visiting,
A little lamb was there,
I picked it up and held it tight,
It didn't seem to care.
Its wool was soft and felt so warm—
Like sunlight on the sand,
And when I gently put it down
It licked me on the hand.

Kim Worthington

On the Grassy Banks

On the grassy banks
Lambkins at their pranks;
Woolly sisters, woolly brothers,
Jumping off their feet,
While their woolly mothers
Watch by them and bleat.

Christina Rossetti

The Lamb

Little Lamb, who made thee?
Dost thou know who made thee?
Gave thee life, and bade thee feed
By the stream and o'er the mead;
Gave thee clothing of delight,
Softest clothing, woolly, bright;
Gave thee such a tender voice,
Making all the vales rejoice?
Little Lamb, who made thee?
Dost thou know who made thee?

William Blake

Mary's Lamb

Mary had a little lamb,
Its fleece was white as snow;
And everywhere that Mary went
The lamb was sure to go.

He followed her to school one day,
Which was against the rule;
It made the children laugh and play
To see a lamb at school.

And so the teacher turned him out,
But still he lingered near,
And waited patiently about
Till Mary did appear.

"What makes the lamb love Mary so?"
The eager children cry.
"Oh, Mary loves the lamb you know,"
The teacher did reply.

Sarah Josepha Hale

L—Lambs

55

L—Letters

The Postman

The whistling postman swings along.
  His bag is deep and wide,
And messages from all the world
  Are bundled up inside.

The postman's walking up our street.
  Soon now he'll ring my bell.
Perhaps there'll be a letter stamped
  In Asia. Who can tell?

Author Unknown

The Postman

Eight o'clock;
The postman's knock!
Five letters for Papa;
  One for Lou,
  And none for you,
And three for dear Mamma.

Christina Rossetti

Waiting for the Postman

Where is the postman?
Where is his whistle?
He's late, he's late, he's late.

He's turning the corner.
His pack is enormous.
No wonder I had to wait.

But he handed me packages,
Letters and postcards,
When I ran down to the gate.

Then I didn't mind
  If the postman was late,
And I didn't mind
  If I had to wait,
For I like to get packages
  Down at the gate.

James S. Tippett

Air Mail

I haven't a stamp or an envelope
To send my love a letter;
I'll give it to a bird and hope
That it will get there better.

Monroe Stearns

Mail

Writing a letter
  Is really quite fun
Because I can mail it
  As soon as it's done.

Marchette Chute

Letter to a Robin in March

Dear robin who has gone away
From snow and icy rain,
We hope you'll soon be coming back
To visit us again.

We've written to the flowers,
The peach tree, and the plum,
To ask *them* back, and all of them
Said they'd be *glad* to come.

Kathryn Worth

57

The Monkeys and the Crocodile

Five little monkeys
  Swinging from a tree;
Teasing Uncle Crocodile,
  Merry as can be.
Swinging high, swinging low,
  Swinging left and right:
"Dear Uncle Crocodile,
  Come and take a bite!"

Five little monkeys
  Swinging in the air;
Heads up, tails up,
  Little do they care.
Swinging up, swinging down,
  Swinging far and near:
"Poor Uncle Crocodile,
  Aren't you hungry, dear?"

Four little monkeys
  Sitting in the tree;
Heads down, tails down,
  Dreary as can be.
Weeping loud, weeping low,
  Crying to each other:
"Wicked Uncle Crocodile,
  To gobble up our brother!"

Laura E. Richards

M—Monkeys

The Monkey's Baby

We saw the monkeys at the Zoo,
The monkey's baby too.

She perched the baby on her knee
For all of us to see.

He looked so soft, so gray and small,
And made no sound at all.

But when she leaped to a higher swing
He made a sudden spring

And with his claw, so thin and frail,
He swung on the end of her tail!

Marion Edey

58

The Moon's the North Wind's Cooky

The Moon's the North Wind's cooky.
He bites it, day by day,
Until there's but a rim of scraps
That crumble all away.

The South Wind is a baker.
He kneads clouds in his den,
And bakes a crisp new moon *that . . . greedy*
North . . . Wind . . . eats . . . again!

Vachel Lindsay

M—The Moon

I See the Moon

I see the moon
And the moon sees me;
God bless the moon,
And God bless me.

Old Rhyme

The White Window

The Moon comes every night to peep
Through the window where I lie:
But I pretend to be asleep;
And watch the Moon go slowly by,
—And she never makes a sound!

She stands and stares! And then she goes
To the house that's next to me,
Stealing by on tippy-toes;
To peep at folk asleep maybe
—And she never makes a sound!

James Stephens

Morning

Everyone is tight asleep,
I think I'll sing a tune,
And if I sing it loud enough
I'll wake up someone—soon!

Myra Cohn Livingston

The Tardy Playmate

Good morning, sky;
Good morning, sun;
Good morning, little winds that run!
Good morning, birds;
Good morning, trees;
And creeping grass, and brownie bees!
How did you find out it was day?
Who told you night had gone away?
I'm wide awake;
I'm up now, too.
I'll be right out to play with you!

Jean Buchanan

Morning Walk

I went out looking;
this is what I found:
        a shell-backed snail
        inside a pail,
my shadow on the ground,
        a stick,
        a brick,
a cat in a tree,
        a dog
        on a log—
and the dog followed me.

James Steel Smith

M—Morning

Supposing

If it were always morning,
    how dreary it would be
never to see the shadow
    circle our apple tree!

If it were sunny always,
    how we should cry aloud
to welcome the first coming
    of even one small cloud!

Elizabeth Coatsworth

60

M—Mother

To My Mother

When I'm a grown-up lady,
The thing I want to do
Is to be a happy mother—
One exactly just like you.

Gina M. Bell

Only One Mother

Hundreds of stars in the pretty sky,
   Hundreds of shells on the shore together,
Hundreds of birds that go singing by,
   Hundreds of lambs in the sunny weather.

Hundreds of dewdrops to greet the dawn,
   Hundreds of bees in the purple clover,
Hundreds of butterflies on the lawn,
   But only one mother the wide world over.

George Cooper

My Mother

I like the way
My mother talks.
I like the way
She laughs and sings.
And oh, I like the way
The way she walks,
As if her feet
Had kind of wings!

Barbara Young

First Thought

See, I have picked you a flower, Mother,
Out of the garden where it grew.
It smells of warm green grass and clover,
It bloomed this morning,
It bloomed for you.

Myra Cohn Livingston

M—Mountains

Mountain Views

Up to the top of the mountain!
Up till we touch the sky
Where trees are small and rocks are bare
And clouds go drifting by.

Up to the top of the mountain
Where we stop to see the view
Which stretches away for thirty miles
And the ridges are long and blue.

Up to the top of the mountain
Where we stop a while and rest
And climb a tower and look away
North, south, and east, and west.

James S. Tippett

If You Live on a Mountain

If you live on a mountain
　　You say, "Oh, dear,
The things people miss
　　When they don't live here!"

Aileen Fisher

God Made the Mountain Very High

God made the mountain very high
So we could climb up near the sky
And look and see what we thought tall
Were very small things after all.

Annette Wynne

62

The City Mouse and the Garden Mouse

The city mouse lives in a house;—
    The garden mouse lives in a bower,
He's friendly with the frogs and toads,
    And sees the pretty plants in flower.

The city mouse eats bread and cheese;—
    The garden mouse eats what he can;
We will not grudge him seeds and stalks
    Poor little timid furry man.

Christina Rossetti

M—The Mouse

Missing

Has anybody seen my mouse?
I opened his box for half a minute,
Just to make sure he was really in it,
And while I was looking, he jumped outside!
I tried to catch him, I tried, I tried . . .
I think he's somewhere about the house.
Has *anyone* seen my mouse?

Uncle John, have you seen my mouse?

Just a small sort of mouse, a dear little brown one,
He came from the country, he wasn't a town one,
So he'll feel all lonely in a London street;
Why, what could he possibly find to eat?

He must be somewhere. I'll ask Aunt Rose:
Have *you* seen a mouse with a woffelly nose?
Oh, somewhere about—
He's just got out . . .

Hasn't *anybody* seen my mouse?

A. A. Milne

The House of the Mouse

The house of the mouse
is a wee little house,
a green little house in the grass,
which big clumsy folk
may hunt and may poke
and still never see as they pass
this sweet little, neat little,
wee little, green little,
cuddle-down hide-away
house in the grass.

Lucy Sprague Mitchell

My Other Name

Jennifer's my other name.
   (It's make-believe
   and just a game.)

I'm really Anne,
But just the same
I'd much
   much
   rather
   have a name
   like Jennifer.

   (So, if you can
   don't call me Anne.)

Myra Cohn Livingston

N—Names

My Name

My name is most especially
The thing they use for calling me.

Myra Cohn Livingston

Pig-Tails and Pony-Tails

Lucy Lou has pig-tails,
Sandra Sue has curls,
Betsy wears a pony-tail
Just like some bigger girls.
Barbara wears a ribbon
To match each colored dress . . .
Little girls have lots of ways
To fix their hair, I guess!

Vivian G. Gouled

Genevieve Jean

This little girl
Is called Genevieve Jean.

She sits in her chair
Like the child of a Queen.

Not a word or a wiggle
Or any such thing.

She is lofty and calm
As the child of a King.

Barbara Young

Gentle Name

Mary is a gentle name
Like the sound of silver bells,
Like a blue and quiet flame,
Like country brooks and ferny smells;
A friendly, wistful name and airy—
Mary.

Selma Robinson

64

Names

If I had a name
Like Joshua Vame
Or Wimple McScumple O'Dodder
Or Burleigh McBee
Or Harkimer Clee,
I wonder if I would feel odder?

Naida Dickson

After the Party

Jonathan Blake
Ate too much cake,
He isn't himself today;
He's tucked up in bed
With a feverish head,
And he doesn't much care to play.

William Wise

Bill

My name is Bill,
I am four years old.
Daddy says I'm silver,
Mother says I'm gold.
I don't know silver,
I don't know gold.
I only know I'm Billy Brown,
Four years old.

J. L. Salzburg

N—Neighbors

Neighbors

The Cobbles live in the house next door,
In the house with the prickly pine.
Whenever I see them, they ask, "How are you?"
And I always answer, "I'm fine."
And I always ask them, "Is Jonathan home?"
(Jonathan Cobble is nine.)
I'm Jonathan Cobble's very best friend
And Jonathan Cobble is mine.

Mary Ann Hoberman

A New Friend

They've taken in the furniture;
I watched them carefully.
I wondered, "Will there be a child
Just right to play with me?"

So I peeked through the garden fence
(I couldn't wait to see).
I found the little boy next door
Was peeking back at me.

Marjorie Allen Anderson

The New Neighbor

Have you had your tonsils out?
  Do you go to school?
Do you know that there are frogs
  Down by Willow Pool?

Are you good at cricket?
  Have you got a bat?
Do you know the proper way
  To feed a white rat?

Are there any apples
  On your apple tree?
Do you think your mother
  Will ask me in to tea?

Rose Fyleman

66

Next-Door People

The next-door people have a bird!
The yellowest you ever heard!
It hops and chirps and sings—and sings!
Aren't next-door people pleasant things!

Mary Carolyn Davies

Neighbors

Neighbors are people who live on your street,
And tell you you're noisy, or naughty, or sweet.
They smile when you're helpful;
  they frown when you're bad.
Neighbors are folks like your mother and dad.

Alma L. Gray

Neighbors

"Tell me what a neighbor is,"
  Jonathan said.
"A neighbor is a person,
  Who brings you homemade bread.

"A neighbor feeds the puppy
  When you are out of town;
And when a rain is blowing up
  She takes your washing down.

"She reads the children stories;
  She lends you extra ice."
Jonathan smiled at Mother:
  "Neighbors are nice!"

Rebecca K. Sprinkle

The Night

The night
  creeps in
  around my head
  and snuggles down
  upon the bed,
  and makes lace pictures
  on the wall
  but doesn't say a word at all.

Myra Cohn Livingston

N—Night

Tomorrow

Tonight
I go to sleep
As you
Will do.
Tomorrow
I'll wake up,
You'll wake up,
And
The new day
Will
Wake up
Too!

Shirley Coran

At Night

Keep a poem in your pocket
and a picture in your head
and you'll never feel lonely
at night when you're in bed.

The little poem will sing to you
the little picture bring to you
a dozen dreams to dance to you
at night when you're in bed.

So—
Keep a picture in your pocket
and a poem in your head
and you'll never feel lonely
at night when you're in bed.

Beatrice Schenk de Regniers

The Firefly Lights His Lamp

Although the night is damp,
The little firefly ventures out,
And slowly lights his lamp.

Unknown (Japanese)

The Friendly Ocean

When I went walking on the shore
The ocean came to greet me,
And all the waves showed they were glad
By running out to meet me.

Then when I shoveled on the beach
The ocean must have spied me,
Because it poured into the holes
And sat right down beside me!

Ernest Holbrook

To Sail

To sail
Is to go
On water,
Tiptoe.

Ida Fasel

Shhhh!

See what I have,
Hold it up to your ear.
Be very quiet,
Then tell what you hear.

You can hear the ocean,
Its rumble and roar.
Yes, it is a sea shell
That was washed ashore.

Grace A. Stephens

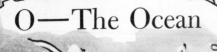

O—The Ocean

An Eraser

My blackboard was
The soft white sand,
Which stretched out far
On every hand.

I searched and found
An empty shell
And wrote out words
That I can spell.

But waves dashed on
The sand to play,
And washed my letters
All away.

And that is how
I got the notion—
A great ERASER
Is the ocean.

Ilo Orleans

69

The Owl and the Pussy-Cat

O—The Owl

The Owl and the Pussy-Cat went to sea
  In a beautiful pea-green boat:
They took some honey, and plenty of money
  Wrapped up in a five-pound note.
The Owl looked up to the stars above,
  And sang to a small guitar,
"O lovely Pussy, O Pussy, my love,
  What a beautiful Pussy you are,
        You are,
        You are!
  What a beautiful Pussy you are!"

Pussy said to the Owl, "You elegant fowl,
  How charmingly sweet you sing!
Oh! let us be married; too long we have tarried:
  But what shall we do for a ring?"
They sailed away, for a year and a day,
  To the land where the bong-tree grows;
And there in a wood a Piggy-wig stood,
  With a ring at the end of his nose,
        His nose,
        His nose,
  With a ring at the end of his nose.

"Dear Pig, are you willing to sell for one shilling
  Your ring?" Said the Piggy, "I will."
So they took it away, and were married next day
  By the Turkey who lives on the hill.
They dined on mince and slices of quince,
  Which they ate with a runcible spoon;
And hand in hand, on the edge of the sand
  They danced by the light of the moon,
        The moon,
        The moon,
  They danced by the light of the moon.

Edward Lear

70

P—Painting

Making a House

First of all, I draw the smoke
        Trailing up the sky;
Then the chimney, underneath;
        And birds all flying by;
Then the house; and every window,
        Watching, like an eye.

Everybody else begins
        With the house. But I
Love the smoke the best of all;
        And you don't know why!
Here it goes,—like little feathers,
        Sailing up the sky!

Josephine Preston Peabody

The Artist

I like to draw
A million scenes
With dogs and planes
And submarines.
I draw them all
So fast that they
Get rather mixed up.
Anyway,
The best of drawing
Things, by far,
Is telling grownups
What they *are*!

Wallace M. Kelly

Outside In

The sky is low, the world is wet.
I'll paint a lovely violet
To brighten up this stormy day,
When I cannot go out to play.
The earth is cold, the sky is gray.
I must stay in, yet I am gay;
For I will paint a shining tree
And have the outside in with me.

Omar Lee Reed

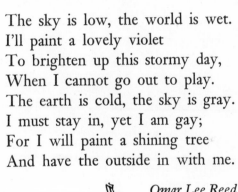

Art

I'm painting a picture,
    A beautiful one,
But no one can see it
    Until it is done.

It isn't an engine.
    It isn't a rose.
And when I will finish it
    Nobody knows.

Marchette Chute

71

P—The Park

Playtime

Little red see-saw!
Watch it go!
At one end is Mary,
At the other end, Joe.

Edna Gray B. MacDonald

Park Bench

A bench is good for this and that—
A useful place to leave a hat,
A handy place for climbing on
Or putting all my dolls upon,
And even good for playing jacks
If I am careful of the cracks.

I could do many things upon it
If people would stop sitting on it.

Marchette Chute

72

I Like to Swing

I start slow
With lazy pushes
And before I know it
I'm clear above the bushes.
Higher and higher, swing wide,
Feels like I have some wings inside!
Then up above the treetops, oh, so high!
At last I'm really sailing, sailing through the sky!

Regina Sauro

The Frozen Fountain

The fountain in our city park
Always dances lightly,
Sending raindrops in the pool,
Sparkling, shining brightly.

But it was so cold last night,
Our playful little fountain
Froze its toes and turned into
A glistening, icy mountain.

Irene U. Hartwell

My Swing

Squeaky, squeaky
Goes my swing.
This is the way
A swing can sing.

Charlotte Steiner

The Merry-Go-Round

The merry-go-round
  whirls round and round
  in a giant circle on the ground.

And the horses run
  an exciting race
  while the wind blows music in your face.

Then the whole world spins
  to a colored tune
  but the ride is over much too soon.

Myra Cohn Livingston

Surprise

Last week I played
Out in the park,
Coasting on my sled.
Today I looked
For snow and found
A violet instead!

Billee Eckert Martin

73

P—Pets

Mrs. Peck-Pigeon

Mrs. Peck-Pigeon
Is picking for bread,
Bob-bob-bob
Goes her little round head.
Tame as a pussy-cat
In the street,
Step-step-step
Go her little red feet.
With her little red feet
And her little round head,
Mrs. Peck-Pigeon
Goes picking for bread.

Eleanor Farjeon

Puppy Work

I had a pair of bright green shoes;
I only wore them Sundays.
My puppy chewed on them one night,
And now I wear them Mondays.

Nancy Eagan

The Animal Store

If I had a hundred dollars to spend,
    Or maybe a little more,
I'd hurry as fast as my legs would go,
    Straight to the animal store.

I wouldn't say, "How much for this or that?"—
    "What kind of a dog is he?"
I'd buy as many as rolled an eye,
    Or wagged a tail at me!

I'd take the hound with the drooping ears
    That sits by himself alone;
Cockers and Cairns and wobbly pups
    For to be my very own.

I might buy a parrot all red and green,
    And the monkey I saw before,
If I had a hundred dollars to spend,
    Or maybe a little more.

Rachel Field

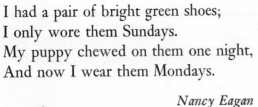

A Baby Bunny

A baby bunny
Is sweet and funny.

Zhenya Gay

Pablo Has a Donkey

Pablo has a donkey
   His ears go floppy-flop!
It's hard to get him started,
   It's hard to make him stop!

Pablo's beast is stubborn,
   He balks at every hill,
At times he's very trying,
   But Pablo loves him still!

Nona Keen Duffy

The House Cat

The house cat sits and smiles and sings,
He knows a lot of secret things.

Annette Wynne

Three Little Turtles

Gwendolyn, Gertrude,
And Gladys are three
Green little turtles
Belonging to me.

They walk very slowly,
The reason I know;
They carry their houses
Wherever they go.

They're all very ladylike,
Prim and polite.
You see, they're so quiet
They're quite a delight!

Gwendolyn, Gertrude,
And Gladys are three
Green little turtles
As good as can be.

Vivian G. Gouled

Little Goldfish

Little goldfish,
Swimming, splashing.
With so much commotion,
Do you think
That you are still
Living in the ocean?

Regina Sauro

A Good Play

We built a ship upon the stairs
All made of back-bedroom chairs,
And filled it full of sofa pillows
To go a-sailing on the billows.

We took a saw and several nails,
And water in the nursery pails;
And Tom said, "Let us also take
An apple and a slice of cake;"—
Which was enough for Tom and me
To go a-sailing on, till tea.

We sailed along for days and days,
And had the very best of plays;
But Tom fell out and hurt his knee,
So there was no one left but me.

Robert Louis Stevenson

Skates

Look who's coming—little Kate!
She is learning how to skate.

Romney Gay

My Day

Rain or shine,
The day is mine.
Now, what shall I do
With my day?

I'll think,
And think,
And think,
And then
I'll play,
And play,
And play.

Barbara Young

Mud-Pies

"Pies for sale! Pies for sale!
Who wants to buy
A nice mud pie?

"Big ones, juicy ones,
Fat ones, oozy ones,
All kinds of pies,
Any, any size.
Sarah's pies are wetter,
But my pies are better.

"Please,
Please, won't you try
A nice mud pie?"

Wymond Bradbury Garthwaite

Playing Ladies

We'll play that we are ladies
    And put on high-heel shoes.
I shall wear the green ones
    And you may wear the blues.

We'll play that we are ladies
    And look through things and choose;
We'll put on costume jewels,
    And wear our high-heel shoes!

Nona Keen Duffy

I Want a Pony

I want a dappled pony.
I'll ride him far away
Across the hills and valleys
Through blossomings of May.

I want a coal-black pony,
Neither wild nor shy,
To carry me through shady lanes
In sweltering July.

I want a small brown pony.
He must not be too sober.
We'll race along the windy roads
In brightly dressed October.

I want a snow-white pony,
His color please remember,
To pull a sleigh on snowy days
In shivering December.

I do so want a pony,
Just any kind at all,
To ride in spring and summer,
In winter and in fall.

James S. Tippett

Trot Along, Pony

Trot along, pony.
  Late in the day,
Down by the meadow
  Is the loveliest way.

The apples are rosy
  And ready to fall.
The branches hang over
  By Grandfather's wall.

But the red sun is sinking
  Away out of sight.
The chickens are settling
  Themselves for the night.

Your stable is waiting
  And supper will come.
So turn again, pony.
  Turn again home.

Marion Edey

P—Ponies

Q—Questions

Questions

A squirrel running across the park
Carried his tail like a question mark.

He carried his tail that way because
He could not remember where something was!

He'd buried a big, delicious nut,
But where, oh where? He had quite forgot.

If he keeps his tail like a question mark,
He'll find the answer (perhaps) by dark.

Miriam Clark Potter

Curiosity

Tell me, tell me everything!
    What makes it Winter
    And then Spring?
    Which are the children
    Butterflies?
    Why do people keep
    Winking their eyes?
    Where do birds sleep?
    Do bees like to sting?
Tell me, tell me please, everything!

Tell me, tell me, I want to know!
    What makes leaves grow
    In the shapes they grow?
    Why do goldfish
    Keep chewing? and rabbits
    Warble their noses?
    Just from habits?
    Where does the wind
    When it goes away go?
Tell me! or don't even grownups know?

Harry Behn

Color

What is pink? a rose is pink
By the fountain's brink.
What is red? a poppy's red
In its barley bed.
What is blue? the sky is blue
Where the clouds float through.
What is white? a swan is white
Sailing in the light.
What is yellow? pears are yellow,
Rich and ripe and mellow.
What is green? the grass is green,
With small flowers between.
What is violet? clouds are violet
In the summer twilight.
What is orange? why, an orange,
Just an orange!

Christina Rossetti

78

Q Is for Quietness

Q is for the Quietness
    Of Sunday avenues
When silence walks the city
    In her pretty velvet shoes;
When trucks forget to rumble,
    And from steeples everywhere
The bells of Sunday morning
    Ring their questions on the air.

Phyllis McGinley

Q—Quietness

The Very Quiet Forest

That night
After the little boy had gone to bed
He wiggled down deep in the soft sheets
And thought about his secret forest

Where everything
Was so quiet
And so soft
And so still.

He closed his eyes
And felt the stillness
And heard the stillness.
And . . . sh -ss -ss -ss -s
Listen——
Do you?

Carolyn Surratt

Tippytoes

Rover's asleep on the floor;
I quietly open the door.
I want to go in without his
        knowing,
And that's why
    I am
        t
          i
            p
              p
              y
                t
                  o
                    e
                      i
                        n
                          g
                          !
shhhh.

Shirley Coran

79

R—Rain

Rain Sizes

Rain comes in various sizes.
Some rain is as small as a mist.
It tickles your face with surprises,
And tingles as if you'd been kissed.

Some rain is the size of a sprinkle
And doesn't put out all the sun.
You can see the drops sparkle and twinkle,
And a rainbow comes out when it's done.

Some rain is as big as a nickel
And comes with a crash and a hiss.
It comes down too heavy to tickle.
It's more like a splash than a kiss.

When it rains the right size and you're wrapped in
Your rainclothes, it's fun out of doors.
But run home before you get trapped in
The big rain that rattles and roars.

John Ciardi

Rain

The rain is raining
all around,
It falls on field
and tree,
It rains on the
umbrellas here,
And on the ships
at sea.

Robert Louis Stevenson

April Shower

The rain comes down so fast
I cannot see the drops.
Then suddenly, it seems,
　It drips . .
　　　and drops . . .
　　　　and stops . . . .

Emily H. Watson

Rain Poem

The rain was like a little mouse,
quiet, small and gray.
It pattered all around the house
and then it went away.

It did not come, I understand,
indoors at all, until
it found an open window and
left tracks across the sill.

Elizabeth Coatsworth

80

No Drip of Rain

It rained on Anne,
it rained on Fan,
it rained on Arabella,
but—
it did not rain
on Mary Jane—
SHE had a HUGE umbrella.

Ivy O. Eastwick

The Busy Windshield Wiper

Snick . . . Snack. Snick . . . Snack.
　It's the windshield wiper rubbing.
He doesn't like rain on his windowpane,
　And he gives each drop a drubbing.

Arthur Kramer

Who Likes the Rain?

"I" said the duck, "I call it fun,
For I have my little red rubbers on;
They make a cunning three-toed track
In the soft cool mud. Quack! Quack! Quack!"

Clara D. Bates

Rain

How does
the rain
have the sense
to know

Winter
is here,
and it's time
to snow?

Aileen Fisher

It Is Raining

It is raining.

Where would you like to be in the rain?
Where would you like to be?

I'd like to be on a city street,
where the rain comes down in a driving sheet,
where it wets the houses—roof and wall—
the wagons and horses and autos and all.
That's where I'd like to be in the rain,
that's where I'd like to be.

Lucy Sprague Mitchell

Wagons

I like wagons better than scooters;
I like wagons better than skates;
Better than bicycles (even those with tooters).
Wagons can be loaded up, with boxes and with crates,
With papers for the paper sale, with dogs that go for rides
(Dogs can pull wagons and carry things, besides).
Wagons can be used for almost everything I do,
And that's why I like wagons best, of things that go—
Don't you?

Dorothy Brown Thompson

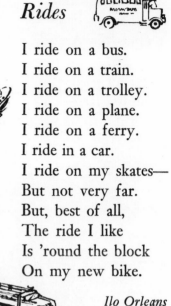

Rides

I ride on a bus.
I ride on a train.
I ride on a trolley.
I ride on a plane.
I ride on a ferry.
I ride in a car.
I ride on my skates—
But not very far.
But, best of all,
The ride I like
Is 'round the block
On my new bike.

Ilo Orleans

Tricycle

I ride on my tricycle every day.
All around the yard,
Pushing, and pushing, and pushing away
Ever and ever so hard!

It's one foot down, and the other foot down,
Round and round, and round,
Tooting, and honking, and ringing my bell
With a whirrity, burrity sound.

Here I go down the hill whizzing so fast,
But I can stop quick if I like;
My feet turn the other way, now I back up!
I go just where I want on my bike.

My tricycle's shiny and bright and red,
And the bell makes a beautiful ding.
Oh, won't you come with me and ride round the yard?
And we'll kick, and we'll toot, and we'll ring!

Rhoda W. Bacmeister

The Race

My tricycle's a camel
With thickly padded feet.

My wagon is a charger
That clatters down the street.

I'd like to ride them both at once
To see which one would beat!

Aileen Fisher

R—Rockets

Outer Space

With whirr and blast, in a rocket ship,
I'll shoot to outer space—
I'll say: "Good-by, dear Mother Earth,
I'm off from place to place!"

It might be fun to whirl about,
Like birds in dizzy flights,
And learn about strange doings
On distant satellites.

Do horses neigh, do bullfrogs croak,
Do cats meow and purr,
On Venus, Mars, or Mercury,
Or far-off Jupiter?

But after I have visited
Along the Milky Way—
How anxious I shall be to get
Back to Earth to stay!

Ilo Orleans

My Rocket Ship

In the rocket ship that I built myself
  From a box, a tub, and a broom,
I flew all the way to the moon today,
  With a rip, a roar, and a boom!

I nodded at Mars, dodged comets and stars,
  Hit the Milky Way with a splash,
Then my silver ship, on its upper lip,
  Wore a curious white mustache!

I had to zip on this dangerous trip,
  But my rocket ship is a winner—
Though I blasted away quite late in the day,
  I was home in time for dinner!

Frances Gorman Risser

Questions ★ ★ ★ ★ ★ ★

When it's storming here on Earth,
Is it lightning up on Mars?
Does it thunder on the Moon?
Does it rain upon the Stars?

I ask myself these questions.
They are things I'd like to know.
And some day in my own space ship
I'll learn whether they are so.

Emily M. Hilsabeck

First Day of School

This is a very special day!
    And if you would like to see
A proud little girl on her way to school,
    Just take a look at me!

Harriet Evatt

September Morning

School is waiting,
Can't be late!
Hurry, hurry!
Half-past eight!
Out the door,
And down the street
Then softly, quietly,
Take your seat.

Katherine Edelman

School Bus

Every morning children wait
By the mailbox, by the gate,
Watching up the windy road
For the school bus and its load.

After the busy hours, after
Accomplishment and friends and laughter,
In the afternoon's falling sun,
The school bus leaves them, one by one.

At tree and crossroad, gate and log,
Greeted by opened doors and dogs,
By cookies, gingerbread and purrs,
Behold the starved adventurers!

Frances Frost

School

Donny likes arithmetic,
    Especially to add.
Connie's good at making pictures
    On a drawing pad.

Larry's fond of history,
    And Mary's good at grammar,
While Terry says it's lots of fun
    To work with saw and hammer.

Milly loves geography.
    But never could you guess
What Billy likes the best of all,
    For Billy likes *recess*!

Florence Logee

School Is Over

School is over,
    Oh, what fun!
Lessons finished,
    Play begun.
Who'll run fastest,
    You or I?
Who'll laugh loudest?
    Let us try.

Kate Greenaway

S—School

Two Little Dragons

Two little dragons
lived in a wood,
　　One was bad,
　　and one was good.

One went walking
straight to school
　　One went fishing
　　in Cranberry Pool.

One learned add-up
and take-away.
　　One spent all of
　　his time in play.

One helped mother
when school was done.
　　One chased little boys
　　just for fun!

If you were a dragon
and lived in a wood,
　　Would you be bad—
　　or would you be good?

Ivy O. Eastwick

Twenty Froggies

Twenty froggies went to school
Down beside a rushy pool;
Twenty little coats of green,
Twenty vests all white and clean.

"We must be in time," said they,
"First we study, then we play;
That is how we keep the rule,
When we froggies go to school."

George Cooper

New Shoes

When I am walking down the street
I do so like to watch my feet.
Perhaps you do not know the news,
Mother has bought me fine new shoes!
When the left one steps I do not speak,
I listen to its happy squeak.

Marjorie Seymour Watts

Old Shoes

I love my very oldest shoes,
They're patched and worn and torn.
And if I had a chance to choose
I'd wear them still—
Perhaps I will!

Zhenya Gay

Sneakers

Feet
   that wear shoes
     Can walk
       and have fun.
Feet
   that wear sneakers
     Want only
       to run.

Lilian Moore

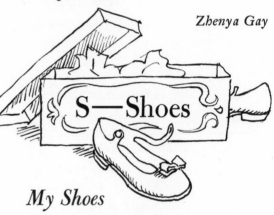

My Shoes

Before I jump into my bed
Before I dim my light,
I put my shoes together
So they can talk at night.

I'm sure they would be lonely
If I tossed one here, one there.
So I put my shoes together
For they are a friendly pair.

Mary Newman

Mr. Minnitt

Mr. Minnitt mends my soles
When I have walked them into holes.

He works in such a funny place
And has a wrinkly, twinkly face.

His hands are brown and hard and thin,
His thread goes slowly out and in.

He cannot walk without a crutch—
I like him very, very much.

Rose Fyleman

S—Shops

Shop Windows

Mother likes the frocks and hats
And pretty stuffs and colored mats.

Daddy never, never looks
At anything but pipes and books.

Auntie's fond of chains and rings
And all the sparkly diamond things.

Richard likes machines the best;
He doesn't care about the rest.

Nannie always loves to stop
In front of every single shop.

But I don't want to wait for a minute
Till we get to the one with the puppy-dogs in it.

Rose Fyleman

To the Barber's Shop

Once a month
With a hop, hop, hop,
Off I go to the
Barber's shop.

Once a month
With a snip, snip, snip,
He cuts my hair
And home I skip.

Kathryn Jackson

Shopping

A bear and a bunny
Had plenty of money.
They went to the store
For carrots and honey.

When the bear and the bunny
Asked: "Carrots and honey?"
The man in the store
Cried: "Where is your money?"

How strange, and how funny!
They *really* had money—
And that's how they bought
Their carrots and honey!

Ilo Orleans

Shopping

I like to hop, and I like to skip,
And I like to go on a shopping trip.

I like to stand by the bookman's shelf
And choose a book all by myself.

Josephine van Dolzen Pease

S—Snow

First Snow

Snow makes whiteness where it falls.
The bushes look like popcorn-balls.
The places where I always play,
Look like something else today.

Marie Louise Allen

Snowy Morning

Every where
   I walk
      And go,
I leave
  My
    Step-marks
     In
      The
       Snow.

Barbara Young

Kitten in the Snow

Where did you go,
Kitten in the snow?
With every step
You left behind
A ribbon of footprints
To unwind.

But where does it
Begin or end,
Little friend?

Elizabeth Coatsworth

The Snowman

We made a snowman in our yard,
Jolly, and round, and fat.
We gave him father's pipe to smoke
And father's battered hat.
We tied a red scarf around his neck,
And in his buttonhole
We stuck a holly spray.
He had black buttons made of coal
He had black eyes, a turned-up nose,
A wide and cheerful grin;
And there he stood in our front yard,
Inviting company in!

Frances Frost

88

Dust of Snow

The way a crow
Shook down on me
The dust of snow
From a hemlock tree

Has given my heart
A change of mood
And saved some part
Of a day I had rued.

Robert Frost

Outside the Door

Outside the door the bare tree stands,
And catches snowflakes in its hands,
And holds them well and holds them high,
Until a puffing wind comes by.

Annette Wynne

My Worn-Out Mittens

My worn-out mittens tell me
That it is almost spring.
I didn't look for green grass
Or hear a robin sing,
But—
When I put on my mittens,
My fingers peek right through.
I think that they are looking
For warm spring days, don't you?

Sally Eggleson

Snow Stars

The starry snowflakes tumble down
On the roof tops
And the town;

While playing in the snowy street,
Snowbirds make star prints
With their feet.

Dorothy Webber Caton

March

March is sometimes
Wet with showers;
Bright sometimes
With sunny hours;
Sometimes windy,
Sometimes gray,
Yet I'm glad
She came today.

Enola Chamberlin

S—Spring

April Song

April is made of
such wonderful things:
Sunbeams and tulips
and butterfly wings,

Cherry-tree blossoms
and little green shoots,
Umbrellas and puddles
and red rubber boots,

Lambs in the meadows
and children in swings;
April is made of
such wonderful things!

Ruth Adams Murray

News of Spring

A dandelion stood tall and yellow,
Spreading the news like a gay young fellow;
And he nodded the word—
"It's spring!"

A robin said that a breeze he knew
Had brought him the message,
And it was true;
And the robin twittered—
"It's spring!"

A cherry blossom unfolded white
As popping corn, on a bough last night;
And waved us below—
"It's spring!"

And we looked at the sky
And the tree
And the ground,
And there—sure enough—
It was spring
All around!

Dorothy Brown Thompson

I Heard It in the Valley

I heard it in the valley,
I heard it in the glen;
Listen, children, surely, surely
Spring is coming back again!

I heard it in the valley,
I heard it on the hill,
I heard it where the bare trees stand,
Very brave and still.

I heard it in the valley—
I heard the waters start,
I heard it surely, surely,
I heard it in my heart!

Annette Wynne

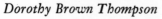

April

The tulips now are pushing up
Like small green knuckles through the ground.
The grass is young and doubtful yet.
The robin takes a look around.
And if you listen you can hear
Spring laughing with a windy sound.

Eunice Tietjens

S—Stars

A Rhyme to Make a Wish On

Star light, star bright,
First star I see tonight;
I wish I may, I wish I might,
Have the wish I wish tonight.

Old Rhyme

The Little Star

Twinkle, twinkle, little star,
How I wonder what you are!
Up above the world so high,
Like a diamond in the sky.

When the blazing sun is set,
And the grass with dew is wet,
Then you show your little light,
Twinkle, twinkle, all the night.

In the dark blue sky you keep,
And often through my curtains peep,
For you never shut your eye
Till the sun is in the sky.

As your bright and tiny spark
Lights the traveler in the dark,
Though I know not what you are,
Twinkle, twinkle, little star.

Jane Taylor

The Star

O little one away so far,
You cannot hear me when I sing.
You cannot tell me what you are,
I cannot tell you anything.

Elizabeth Madox Roberts

Candle Star

A candle looked up at the sky and said,
"What is it like to be a star?"
A star smiled down from overhead
And said, "You are."

Lourena Renton Brown

Neighbors

The newest moon is not so far
From a small and friendly evening star;
When day has gone and the sun is out,
What do you think they talk about?

Do they speak of the curious things of sky?
Of the time when a comet whistled by?
Or do they whisper across the air,
"Who is that little girl down there?"

Anne Blackwell Payne

The Falling Star

I saw a star slide down the sky,
Blinding the north as it went by,
Too burning and too quick to hold,
Too lovely to be bought or sold,
Good only to make wishes on
And then forever to be gone.

Sara Teasdale

Stars

Stars
burn so brightly when they glow
I
wonder where their ashes go.

Aileen Fisher

93

Clatter Street

Lindy lived on Clatter Street,
Clatter Street, Clatter Street,
Lindy lived on Clatter Street,
Where all the world goes by.

Why does she live on Clatter Street,
Clatter Street, Clatter Street,
Why does she live on Clatter Street,
Oh, can you tell me why?

Why, Lindy loves her Clatter Street,
Clatter Street, Clatter Street,
Why, Lindy loves her Clatter Street,
And that's the reason why.

Leroy F. Jackson

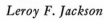

The City Goes

All around about the Town
The streets go up,
The streets go down.
Across and back
And round about,
The streets go winding
In and out.

The City goes
So wide and far!
And like a rainbow
Or a star,
I cannot see
Around the bend.
I wonder
Does it
Have an end?

Barbara Young

Away We Go!

Hippity-hop!
Skippity-skop!
We've hopped so long
Our feet won't stop.

We say hello
To those we meet
And hippity-hop
On down the street!

Eleanor Dennis

Friday Street

Where shall we meet, O where shall we meet?
We'll meet to be sure in Friday Street.

Shall we meet on Saturday?—O dear no!
On Saturday, on Saturday I have to knead the dough.

Shall we meet on Sunday?—O dear no!
On Sunday, on Sunday to church I must go.

Shall we meet on Monday?—O dear no!
On Monday I wash linen as white as driven snow.

Shall we meet on Tuesday?—O dear no!
On Tuesday I darn the socks, heel and toe.

Shall we meet on Wednesday?—O dear no!
On Wednesday I've a meadowful of grass to mow.

Shall we meet on Thursday?—O dear no!
On Thursday my best bonnet wants a new satin bow.

Then when shall we meet, O when shall we meet?
On Friday to be sure in Friday Street.

Eleanor Farjeon

Street Mending

The men on the corner are digging a ditch
Or fixing the paving—I don't know which.
And in a big box they are making mud pies!
I think they need help from someone my size!

Dorothy Faubion

City Street at Night

A city street at night
Is a fascinating sight.
    I like to watch the antics
        Of the signs:

I like the jolly winking,
The unexpected blinking
    Of the buildings all ablaze
        With gay designs.

Nona Keen Duffy

95

S—Summer

Song of Summer

Golden sun,
Golden air,
Golden blossoms
Everywhere!

Up and down
The shining land
Is a bright-eyed
Lively band,
Sun-warmed,
Honey-brown—
On plain and hill,
On shore and town.

Golden sun,
Golden air,
Golden children
Everywhere!

Ethel Jacobson

Looking for Summer

I went upon a sunny way
Looking for Summer, yesterday.
I found her standing like a tree,
And she was lovely, O to see.
She wore her greenness like a crown,
And at her feet I sat me down.

Barbara Young

A June Day

I heard a red-winged blackbird singing
  Down where the river sleeps in the reeds;
That was morning, and at noontime
  A hummingbird flashed on the jewelweeds;
Clouds blew up, and in the evening
  A yellow sunset struck through the rain,
Then blue night, and the day was ended
  That never will come again.

Sara Teasdale

That's July

A bunch of grass, a wild rose,
  A bird that's learned to fly,
Children out for holiday,—
  That's July.

Mary F. Butts

Summer Grass

Summer grass aches and whispers.

It wants something;
it calls out and sings;
it pours out wishes to the overhead stars.

The rain hears;
the rain answers;
the rain is slow coming;
the rain wets the face of the grass.

Carl Sandburg

August Smiles

August is a lazy girl—
lazy and yet sweet,
fingers stained with raspberries,
slippers off her feet.

August doesn't care for work,
doesn't care for sport,
doesn't like too serious talk,
bicker or retort,

likes to lie in grasses green,
half-asleep, beguiling.
When you wake her from her doze,
August wakens, smiling.

Elizabeth Coatsworth

End-of-Summer Poem

The little songs of summer are all gone today.
The little insect instruments are all packed away:
The bumblebee's snare drum, the grasshopper's guitar,
The katydid's castanets—I wonder where they are.
The bullfrog's banjo, the cricket's violin,
The dragonfly's cello have ceased their merry din.
Oh, where is the orchestra? From harpist down to drummer
They've all disappeared with the passing of summer.

Rowena Bennett

T—Thanksgiving

First Thanksgiving of All

Peace and Mercy and Jonathan,
And Patience (very small),
Stood by the table giving thanks
The first Thanksgiving of all.
There was very little for them to eat,
Nothing special and nothing sweet;
Only bread and a little broth,
And a bit of fruit (and no tablecloth);
But Peace and Mercy and Jonathan
And Patience, in a row,
Stood up and asked a blessing on
Thanksgiving, long ago.
Thankful they were their ship had come
Safely across the sea;
Thankful they were for hearth and home,
And kin and company;
They were glad of broth to go with their bread,
Glad their apples were round and red,
Glad of mayflowers they would bring
Out of the woods again next spring.
So Peace and Mercy and Jonathan,
And Patience (very small),
Stood up gratefully giving thanks
The first Thanksgiving of all.

Nancy Byrd Turner

Thanksgiving Song of a Little Mouse

For the crumbs I find
Most every day,
And the cheese that sometimes
Comes my way,
For a good dark hole
Too small for a cat,
And for silent feet,
And a long tail that
Helps me balance
As I run,
And for all of my
Gray-fur, mousy fun—
I'm thankful!

Solveig Paulson Russell

Thanksgiving

For each new morning with its light,
    Father, we thank Thee,
For rest and shelter of the night,
    Father, we thank Thee,
For health and food, for love and friends,
For everything Thy goodness sends,
    Father, in heaven, we thank Thee.

Ralph Waldo Emerson

Thanksgiving Day

Over the river and through the wood,
To Grandfather's house we go;
The horse knows the way
To carry the sleigh
Through the white and drifted snow.

Over the river and through the wood,
Oh, how the wind does blow!
It stings the toes
And bites the nose
As over the ground we go.

Over the river and through the wood,
Trot fast, my dapple-gray!
Spring over the ground
Like a hunting hound!
For this is Thanksgiving Day.

Over the river and through the wood,
Now Grandmother's cap I spy!
Hurrah for the fun!
Is the pudding done?
Hurrah for the pumpkin pie!

Lydia Maria Child

99

T—Toys

The Drum

The drum's a quiet little fellow
When he's left alone.
But, oh, how he does roar and bellow,
Rattle snap and groan,

Clatter, spatter, dash and patter,
Rumble, shriek and moan,
Whene'er I take my sticks in hand
And beat him soundly for the band!

John Farrar

The New Doll

I love your face,
I love your hands,
I love your shining hair.
I love the way you tilt your head,
I love the clothes you wear.
I love your lashes
On your cheek,
I love your little smile.
I'm sure you'll love me, too, when I
Have cared for you awhile.

Dorothy Faubion

Looking Forward

When I am grown to man's estate
I shall be very proud and great,
And tell the other girls and boys
Not to meddle with my toys.

Robert Louis Stevenson

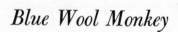

Blue Wool Monkey

The blue wool monkey won't sit where
We put him in the rocking chair.

He likes it better on my bed
Where he can tumble on his head

And somersault upon the floor
To see who's coming in the door.

Myra Cohn Livingston

My Top

I've finally gotten my top,
I know it's the best on the block.
It's red and it's thin,
The tip is of tin,
It's the last
Of them all
to
S
T
O
P

Jeanne L. Kenyon

The Shop Across the Street

I know a little toy shop
That has the nicest things;
Their bats and balls are very fine,
Their skates will give you wings.

Next week I'll have a birthday
And for a special treat,
I may choose what I would like the best
In the shop across the street.

Mary A. Gilliam

Soap Bubbles

Dip the pipe in the suds just so;
Lift it out, and gently blow—
Dip and blow,
Dip and blow—
And through the air the bubbles go!

Bubbles, floating—see them fall,
Each a shiny little ball.
Float and fall,
Float and fall;
And then they burst—and that is all!

Marie Louise Allen

Outgrown Toys

Last year I got a scooter.
This year I want a "bike."
Next year I'll get a pony.
(At least that's what I'd like.)

I outgrow all my presents
The way I do my clothes.
I wish folks would remember
That a little boy grows.

Kate Cox Goddard

T—Trains

The Station

The station is a busy place,
With miles and miles of trains,
That run all day and every night
And even when it rains.

There's lots and lots of people there,
With bags and boxes too,
And lots of men to carry them,
All dressed alike in blue.

And when you hear the whistle blow,
Along there comes a train,
And everyone calls out goodbye,
And kisses me again.

Kitty Parsons

Travel

The railroad track is miles away,
    And the day is loud with voices speaking,
Yet there isn't a train goes by all day
    But I hear its whistle shrieking.

All night there isn't a train goes by,
    Though the night is still for sleep and dreaming,
But I see its cinders red on the sky,
    And hear its engine steaming.

My heart is warm with the friends I make,
    And better friends I'll not be knowing,
Yet there isn't a train I wouldn't take,
    No matter where it's going.

Edna St. Vincent Millay

The Local

At the end of the lake,
    the train goes past.
It's not very big,
    but it goes very fast.

It hurries and chuffs
    (though it's not very big!)
Like a little cross man
    in a white curly wig.

Elizabeth Coatsworth

Little Black Train

Little black train
On a long steel track.
Come back; Come back;
But the train goes on
Till the train is gone.

Margaret Wise Brown

102

The Red Caboose

It's fun to watch the freight train
  Come whistling round the bend.
A shaky little red caboose
  Is fastened to the end.

The engine puffs and pulls and pants
  And whistles loud and long;
The wheels of all the cars go round
  With a clicky-clacky song.

When I grow up to be a man,
  Some day I'm going to ride
On that shaky little red caboose
  And find out what's inside!

Lucia Cabot

Song of the Train

Clickety-clack,
Wheels on the track,
This is the way
They begin the attack:
Click-ety-clack,
Click-ety-clack,
Click-ety, *clack*-ety,
Click-ety
Clack.

Clickety-clack,
Over the crack,
Faster and faster
The song of the track:
Clickety-clack,
Clickety-clack,
Clickety, clackety,
Clackety,
Clack.

Riding in front,
Riding in back,
Everyone hears
The song of the track:
Clickety-clack,
Clickety-clack,
Clickety, *clickety*,
Clackety
Clack.

David McCord

Trains at Night

I like the whistle of trains at night,
The fast trains thundering by so proud!
They rush and rumble across the world,
They ring wild bells and they toot so loud!

But I love better the slower trains.
They take their time through the world instead,
And whistle softly and stop to tuck
Each sleepy blinking town in bed!

Frances Frost

103

The Friendly Tree

I wanted a tree
For shade and rest,
I wanted a tree
Where a robin could nest.

So I planted a flowering
Friendly tree
For myself, and a bird,
And a honeybee!

Mabel Watts

T—Trees

Every Time I Climb a Tree

Every time I climb a tree
Every time I climb a tree
Every time I climb a tree
I scrape a leg
Or skin a knee
And every time I climb a tree
I find some ants
Or dodge a bee
And get the ants
All over me.

And every time I climb a tree
Where have you been?
They say to me
But don't they know that I am free
Every time I climb a tree?

David McCord

Tree Language

Though trees keep whispering all the day,
    I still am left without
One tiny clue to let me know
    The things they talk about.

Katherine Edelman

104

Trees

Trees are the kindest things I know,
They do no harm, they simply grow

And spread a shade for sleepy cows,
And gather birds among their boughs.

They give us fruit in leaves above,
And wood to make our houses of,

And leaves to burn on Halloween,
And in the Spring new buds of green.

They are the first when day's begun
To touch the beams of morning sun,

They are the last to hold the light
When evening changes into night,

And when a moon floats on the sky
They hum a drowsy lullaby

Of sleepy children long ago . . .
Trees are the kindest things I know.

Harry Behn

Winter Trees

There's one leaf left
    On the tip of our tree;
And across the street
    Their tree has three.

Now I wonder why
    A dozen or more
Are still left on
    The tree next door.

Mildred Dingle Reed

105

U—Umbrellas

The New Umbrella

I have a new umbrella
That can go up or down,
A pretty, red umbrella
That Mother bought in town.

On all the sunny, bright days
It stays folded safe away,
But I take it out to carry
On every rainy day.

It opens like a big red flower
A lovely thing to see,
And I walk under, through the rain,
As dry as dry can be!

Rhoda W. Bacmeister

U Is for Umbrellas

U is for Umbrellas
    That bloom in rainy weather,
Like many-colored mushrooms,
    Sprouting upward altogether.
How useful an umbrella is!
    But still I often wonder
If a roof on stormy evenings
    Isn't nicer to be under.

Phyllis McGinley

Umbrellas

See them bobbing
Up and down:
Wet umbrellas, red and brown,
Blue and crossbarred,
Green and black,
Up the slippery street and back.

Tumbling wind
That romps about
Sometimes turns one inside out;
Pulling, tugging,
Playing clown.
(We are upstairs, looking down.)

Clarice Foster Booth

A Dog and a Cat Went Out Together

A dog and a cat went out together
To see some friends just out of town;
Said the cat to the dog,
"What d'ye think of the weather?"
"I think ma'am the rain will come down;
But don't be alarmed, for I've an umbrella
That will shelter us both," said this amiable fellow.

Old Rhyme

The Elf and the Dormouse

Under a toadstool crept a wee elf,
Out of the rain, to shelter himself.

Under the toadstool sound asleep,
Sat a big dormouse all in a heap.

Trembled the wee elf, frightened, and yet
Fearing to fly away lest he get wet.

To the next shelter—maybe a mile!
Sudden the wee elf smiled a wee smile,

Tugged till the toadstool toppled in two,
Holding it over him, gaily he flew.

Soon he was safe home, dry as could be;
Soon woke the dormouse—"Good gracious me!

"Where is my toadstool?" loud he lamented.
—And that's how umbrellas first were invented.

Oliver Herford

107

V—Vacation

I Want to Go Traveling

I want to go UP;
I want to go DOWN;
I want to go traveling
All around the town.

I want to go HERE;
I want to go THERE;
I want to see the Circus;
I want to see the Fair.

I want to go LEFT;
I want to go RIGHT;
I want to find acorns;
I want to fly a kite.

I want to go EAST;
I want to go WEST;
I want to lie down
For a good long rest.

Ilo Orleans

Ready for a Holiday

My hair is brushed
And very neat.
My best black shoes
Are on my feet.
My dress is pressed,
I look my best.
I'm going away,
It's a holiday.

Zhenya Gay

Vacation at the Seashore

We watch the boats go slowly by
Our cottage at the sea,
And I see each one, with its great white sail,
But the sailors can't see me.

Gabrielle Waugh

Vacation Advice

Have a grand vacation,
And then, before it ends,
Please buy some picture post cards
To send home to all your friends.

Mabel Watts

Highways

Made smooth
    for travel
        with tar
            and gravel
Up hill and down
From town to town
    The highways run.

Some have
    a number
        some have
            a name
On a road map I mark those
Along which we came.
    I think it fun.

James S. Tippett

Traveler

The road that rambles past our house
    Cuts through the fields and thickets,
And never stops for cat or mouse,
    Nor hears the singing crickets.

Exactly how it started out
    I have no way of knowing.
But when I'm twenty-one, about,
    I'll find out where it's going!

Ray Romine

Vacation Time

Vacation is a magic time
    For those who love to roam;
But once a sailor said to me,
(Full seven times he's sailed the sea)
    "There's magic, too, at home."

Rowena Bennett

109

V—Valentines

When You Send a Valentine

When you send a valentine—
That's the time for fun!
Push it underneath the door,
Ring the bell and run, run, run!
Ring the bell and run!

Mildred J. Hill

The Rose Is Red, the Violet's Blue

The rose is red, the violet's blue,
The honey's sweet, and so are you.
Thou art my love, and I am thine;
I drew thee for my Valentine:
The lot was cast, and then I drew,
And fortune said it should be you.

Old Rhyme

To My Valentine

If apples were pears,
And peaches were plums,
And the rose had a different name,—
If tigers were bears,
And fingers were thumbs,
I'd love you just the same!

Author Unknown

School Valentine Box

There's a place to put mail, extra-wide, extra-long.
It can hold quite a lot, for it's sturdy and strong.
And envelopes colored, and envelopes white,
Go dropping and dropping in there, out of sight.

We watch and we count as another slips in—
A square one, a long one, a fat one, a thin.
Tomorrow we'll open it. Hurry up, clocks!
Race round to the time for the Valentine Box!

Dorothy Brown Thompson

Making Valentines

On my valentines I place
    Flowers, hearts, and paper lace.
Hearts and flowers go together
Even in the coldest weather!

Nina Willis Walker

111

W—Wind

Winds A'Blowing

The North Wind is a beggar
Who shudders at the cold.
The South Wind is a sailor
With pockets full of gold.
The East Wind is a gypsy
With saucy cap and feather.
The West Wind is a wizard
Who conjures wicked weather.

The Winter Wind's a giant
As grumpy as a bear.
The Summer Wind's a lady
With flowers in her hair.
The Autumn Wind's an old man
As touchy as a thistle.
The Spring Wind is a gay lad
Who blows a silver whistle.

May Justus

Fishermen's Weather

When the wind is in the East,
'Tis neither good for man nor beast;
When the wind is in the North,
The skillful fisher goes not forth;
When the wind is in the South,
It blows the bait in the fishes' mouth;
When the wind is in the West,
Then the fishes bite the best.

Old Rhyme

The Wind

The wind, O the wind, it is made out of air
That always is rushing to get somewhere.
It comes in a hurry,
And goes in a flurry—
It pushes so hard that it makes us all scurry!

It whirls and it twirls
And it tugs at my curls;

It puffs and it blows, and away then it goes!
But why must it hurry? Not anyone knows!

Marie Louise Allen

Little Wind

Little wind, blow on the hilltop;
Little wind, blow down the plain;
Little wind, blow up the sunshine,
Little wind, blow off the rain.

Kate Greenaway

112

Who Has Seen the Wind?

Who has seen the wind?
　Neither I nor you:
But when the leaves hang trembling
　The wind is passing through.

Who has seen the wind?
　Neither you nor I:
But when the trees bow down their heads
　The wind is passing by.

Christina Rossetti

The Wind

Where the Wind blows
It sows, it sows!
Seed scatters,
Grass grows,
Earth starts,
Water flows,
And Polly's Cheek is like a Rose.

Eleanor Farjeon

Windy Nights

Whenever the moon and stars are set,
　Whenever the wind is high,
All night long in the dark and wet,
　A man goes riding by.
Late in the night when the fires are out,
Why does he gallop and gallop about?

Whenever the trees are crying aloud,
　And ships are tossed at sea,
By, on the highway, low and loud,
　By at the gallop goes he.
By at the gallop he goes, and then
By he comes back at the gallop again.

Robert Louis Stevenson

Wind on the Hill

No one can tell me,
Nobody knows,
Where the wind comes from,
　Where the wind goes.

A. A. Milne

W—Winter

January

When it's January weather
It doesn't matter whether
There is snow or only ice—
Either one is very nice.

Romney Gay

And It Is Cold

I'm bundled up in winter clothes,
Mittens, scarves, and woolen hose,
Tasseled cap, and goodness knows
All that's showing is my nose!

Regina Sauro

I Heard a Bird Sing

I heard a bird sing
  In the dark of December
A magical thing
  And sweet to remember.

"We are nearer to Spring
  Than we were in September,"
I heard a bird sing
  In the dark of December.

Oliver Herford

Mittens

I like the way my
    fingers feel
Inside my mitten—
    only
Sometimes I wonder
    if my thumb
Doesn't get quite
    lonely.

Lilian Moore

114

Winter in the Wood

Snow falls
flake on flake
on the meadow,
on the lake,
on the bleak
and frozen ground . . .
Snow falls
without a sound.
Kingfisher has flown away!
Chaffinch left us
yesterday!
Weasel's hiding
in his hole!
So is Rabbit!
So is Mole!
Fox is lying
low, my dear . . .
Only Robin
still is here!

Ivy O. Eastwick

Winter Trees

I wonder if the trees feel sad
When they're all bare,
And very glad
When new leaves start
To bud and sprout,
And summer-happy
When they're out?

Kathryn Jackson

February Twilight

I stood beside a hill
    Smooth with new-laid snow,
A single star looked out
    From the cold evening glow.

There was no other creature
    That saw what I could see—
I stood and watched the evening star
    As long as it watched me.

Sara Teasdale

Just a Mile Beyond

Winter's house is cold and white,
    but just a mile beyond
Spring lives in a new green house
    beside a sparkly pond.

Aileen Fisher

One Thing at a Time

Work while you work,
Play while you play;
That is the way
To be happy and gay.

All that you do,
Do with your might;
Things done by halves
Are never done right.

One thing at a time
And that done well,
Is a very good rule
As many can tell.

Moments are useless
Trifled away;
So work while you work
And play while you play.

M. A. Stoddart

Wash the Dishes

Wash the dishes, wipe the dishes,
Ring the bell for tea;
Three good wishes, three good kisses,
I will give to thee.

Old Rhyme

W —Work

Setting the Table

Evenings
When the house is quiet
I delight
To spread the white
Smooth cloth and put the flowers on the table.

I place the knives and forks around
Without a sound.
I light the candles.

I love to see
Their small reflected torches shine
Against the greenness of the vine
And garden.

Is that the mignonette, I wonder,
Smells so sweet?

And then I call them in to eat.

Dorothy Aldis

Pretend

It seems to help when I do my work,
    Such as dishes or making my bed,
If I forget I'm a little girl
    And play that I'm Mother instead.

Florance M. Chamberlin

116

Automobile Mechanics

Sometimes
  I help my dad
Work on our automobile.
  We unscrew
  The radiator cap
    And we let some water run—
    Swish—from a hose
    Into the tank.

And then we open up the hood
And feed in oil
From a can with a long spout.
And then we take a lot of rags
And clean all about.
  We clean the top
  And the doors
  And the fenders and the wheels
  And the windows and floors. . . .
    We work *hard*
    My dad
    And I.

              Dorothy W. Baruch

Toolbox

My toolbox is a wishing box.
  I make a wish or two,
Then open it and take some tools
  And make my wish come true.

              Author Unknown

I Meant to Do My Work Today

I meant to do my work today—
But a brown bird sang in the apple tree,
And a butterfly flitted across the field,
And all the leaves were calling me.

And the wind went sighing over the land,
Tossing the grasses to and fro,
And a rainbow held out its shining hand—
So what could I do but laugh and go?

              Richard Le Gallienne

W—The World

The World

All the things you know
and all the things you do
are part of the world.
The world is you!

Betty Miles

Ring Around the World

Ring around the world
Taking hands together
All across the temperate
And the torrid weather.
Past the royal palm-trees
By the ocean sand
Make a ring around the world
Taking each other's hand;
In the valleys, on the hill,
Over the prairie spaces,
There's a ring around the world
Made of children's friendly faces.

Annette Wynne

Around the World

In gocart so tiny
  My sister I drew;
And I've promised to draw her
  The wide world through.

We have not yet started—
  I own it with sorrow—
Because our trip's always
  Put off till tomorrow.

Kate Greenaway

Happy Thought

The world is so full of a number of things,
I'm sure we should all be as happy as kings.

Robert Louis Stevenson

It's Nice to Know

It's nice to know when I'm in bed
That across the world
It's day instead—
And children there are having fun,
While it's their turn
To have the sun.

Kathryn Jackson

The Wide, Wide World

We have a globe in our front hall,
With all the world around it;
And rivers running up and down.
I'm glad my daddy found it!

Kitty Parsons

The World's So Big

Think of all the people
I'll never get to know
because the world's so big
and my scooter's so slow.

Think of all the places
I'll never get to see
because the street's so long
and Mother's calling me!

Aileen Fisher

X — x

X Is 'Xcavation

X is 'Xcavation.
　When a building's being made,
It's almost as exciting
　As an extra big parade.
So even busy grownups
　Will stand in pouring rains,
Examining the dump-trucks
　And the shovels and the cranes.

Phyllis McGinley

X & Y

Y is a chesty letter,
X is an active one.
Y couldn't stand up better,
X seems to walk or run.

David McCord

X Is for X

X is for X
And X marks the spot
On the rug in the parlor,
The sand in the lot,
Where once you were standing,
And now you are not.

William Jay Smith

Fun from A to Z

I'm very fond of X,
He's such a little mark.
He crosses in the middle
Like a pathway in the park.

Y holds his hands above his head,
And never lets them drop,
I know when I have come to Y,
It's almost time to stop.

Poor zigzag Z's the very last,
He's awfully far away,
I really should be nice to him
And put him up with A.

Frances S. Copley

Y—The Year

The Year

January brings the snow,
Makes our feet and fingers glow.

February brings the rain,
Thaws the frozen lake again.

March brings breezes sharp and chill,
To stir the dancing daffodil.

April brings the primrose sweet,
Scatters daisies at our feet.

May brings flocks of pretty lambs,
Skipping by their fleecy dams.

June brings tulips, lilies, roses,
Fills the children's hands with posies.

Hot July brings cooling showers,
Apricots and gillyflowers.

August brings the sheaves of corn;
Then the harvest home is borne.

Clear September brings blue skies,
Goldenrod, and apple pies.

Brown October brings the pheasant,
Then to gather nuts is pleasant.

Dull November brings the blast;
Then the leaves are whirling fast.

Chill December brings the sleet,
Blazing fire and Christmas treat.

Sara Coleridge

121

A New Year

Here's a clean year,
  A white year.
    Reach your hand and take it.

You are
  The builder,
    And no one else can make it.

See what it is
  That waits here,
    Whole and new;

It's not a year only,
  But a world
    For You!

Mary Carolyn Davies

In Trust

It's coming, boys,
  It's almost here;
It's coming, girls,
  The grand New Year!

A year to be glad in,
Not to be bad in;
A year to live in,
To gain and give in;
A year for trying,
And not for sighing;
A year for striving,
And hearty thriving;
A bright new year.
Oh! hold it dear;
For God who sendeth
He only lendeth.

Mary Mapes Dodge

Four Seasons

Springtime is a green time
  When seedlings start their growing.
Summertime's a rainbow time
  When many blooms are blowing.
Autumntime's a brown time
  When seeds are ripe for sowing;
But wintertime's a white time
(It is the flowers' nighttime)
  When stars of frost are glowing.

Rowena Bennett

The Months

Thirty days hath September,
April, June, and November;
All the rest have thirty-one
Excepting February alone,
And that has twenty-eight days clear
And twenty-nine in each leap year.

Old Rhyme

The Year

Summer sunshine,
  Autumn gold,
Blessed Christmas,
  Bright and cold;
Flowers that follow
  April rain,
Good-by all, but
  Come again—
  Oh, come again!

Mary A. Lathbury

Z—The Zoo

Excuse Us, Animals in the Zoo

Excuse us, Animals in the Zoo,
I'm sure we're very rude to you;
Into your private house we stare
And never ask you if you care;
And never ask you if you mind.
Perhaps we really are not kind;
I think it must be hard to stay
And have folks looking in all day,
I wouldn't like my house that way.

Excuse us, Animals in the Zoo,
I'm sure we're very rude to you;
Suppose you all to our house came
And stared at us and called our name.
I hardly think we'd like it at all
In a house that didn't have a wall.
No wonder you pace up and down the floor
And growl a little or even roar—
I'm sure if 'twere we, we'd growl much more.

Excuse us, Animals in the Zoo,
I'm sure we're very rude to you.

Annette Wynne

Lovely Lion

Lovely Lion in the zoo,
Walking by on padded feet
To and fro and fro and to,
Are you wondering what to eat?
Would you like a bowl of stew,
Or a juicy steak, or would
A great big bone be fun to chew?

Or do you think that I look good?

Dorothy Aldis

The Camel

The camel has a single hump;
The dromedary, two;
Or else the other way around.
I'm never sure. Are you?

Ogden Nash

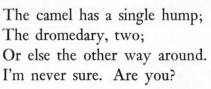

The Hippopotamus

Why make so much fuss
  About a hippopotamus?
He's full of cheer
  From his front to his rear,
    Which, I really must say,
      Looks much the same way.

Zhenya Gay

Llama

Every baby llama
Always has a mama.
It has a papa, too.
But I saw just the mama
With her baby llama
When I was at the Zoo.

Emily M. Hilsabeck

Z Was a Zebra

Z was a zebra,
All striped white and black;
And if he were tame,
You might ride on his back.

Z

Pretty striped zebra!

Edward Lear

Lost at the Zoo

If I were lost
Inside the zoo,
I think that this
Is what I'd do.

I'd say, "Giraffe,
Please look around—
Your head is high
Above the ground.

"Will you point out
To me the place
Where you can see
My mother's face?"

I'm sure Giraffe
Would find my mama,
Looking at an elk
Or llama.

I'd leap to her
Like a kangaroo,
And never get lost
Again at the zoo!

Ilo Orleans

125

At the Zoo

There are lions and roaring tigers, and enormous camels and things,
There are biffalo-buffalo-bisons, and a great big bear with wings,
There's a sort of a tiny potamus, and a tiny nosserus too—
But *I* gave buns to the elephant when *I* went down to the Zoo!

There are badgers and bidgers and bodgers, and a Super-in-tendent's House,
There are masses of goats, and a Polar, and different kinds of mouse,
And I think there's a sort of a something which is called a wallaboo—
But *I* gave buns to the elephant when *I* went down to the Zoo!

If you try to talk to the bison, he never quite understands;
You can't shake hands with a mingo—he doesn't like shaking hands.
And lions and roaring tigers *hate* saying, "How do you do?"—
But *I* give buns to the elephant when *I* go down to the Zoo!

A. A. Milne

126

Index of Authors

Index of Titles

Index of First Lines

133

135

ILLUSTRATIONS BY CHARLES AND DOROTHEA FOX
AND WINIFRED W. COFFIN

A B C D E F G H I J 06987654
PRINTED IN THE UNITED STATES OF AMERICA